The Story of
NURSING

THE STORY OF
NURSING

by Bertha S. Dodge

ILLUSTRATED BY
BARBARA CORRIGAN

Little, Brown and Company · Boston

Published simultaneously
in Canada by McClelland and Stewart Limited

PRINTED IN THE UNITED STATES OF AMERICA

To

LAURA REBECCA LOGAN
leader in nursing education

this book
is affectionately
dedicated

Foreword

This book, which attempts to touch upon the highlights of American nursing, past and present, could not have been undertaken without the sympathetic and generous help of many people. The acknowledgment of this help is the author's privilege and obligation. Before mentioning any specific names, it is important to emphasize that no living person whose name was not definitely mentioned is to be regarded as the model for anyone in this book. For instance, it would be unfair both to the individual and to the nursing profession to record word by word an interview with any single student out of the thousands studying nursing today. Center City is a synthetic metropolis and the nurses working there are composites. Only thus can one hope to give a true picture of nursing.

With this preamble, it is perhaps safe to make special acknowledgments. Miss Laura Logan, director of the nursing school and services of the St. Louis City Hospital, and Miss Florence M. Clarke, director of the nursing school and services of the Kansas City General Hospital, were particularly generous in throwing open their schools and services and in providing nurse guides from their very busy staffs. Miss Margaret W. Thomas, Regional Nursing Consultant, Children's Bureau, United States Department of Health, Education, and Welfare, was most helpful in giving her time and making suggestions. The biographical sketch of Estelle Massey Osborne was written after a personal consultation in which Mrs. Osborne gave most generously of her time and advice, and for this kindness the author wishes to express her deep appreciation. To many younger nurses working in hospitals and elsewhere, the author is also deeply indebted.

For advice on matters bacteriological and immunological, thanks are due to Dr. Carroll W. Dodge of Washington University, St. Louis.

Miss Attalee Buckingham, assistant director of the school of nursing of the St. Louis City Hospital, gave much help in the initial stages of making up a bibliography of nursing history; for the loan of many books, the author must express her appreciation.

Special mention should be made of permission to quote from copyrighted material. Mrs. Mary Breckinridge of the Frontier Nursing Service took time out of her very busy schedule to write a letter and send material — bulletins of the Frontier Nursing Service and its descriptive circular, from which the author received permission to quote as she might see fit. The publishers have been kind enough to grant permission to quote from the following books:

Mary Williams Brinton. *My Cap and My Cape: An Autobiography*. Philadelphia: Dorrance & Co., 1950.

Julia O. Flikke. *Nurses in Action, the Story of the Army Nurse Corps*. Philadelphia and New York: J. B. Lippincott Co., 1943.

Anne A. Williamson. *50 Years in Starch*. Culver City, California: Murray & Gee, Inc., 1948.

The California Lutheran Hospital, which holds the copyright on Miss Williamson's book, gave permission to quote therefrom through its director, Mr. L. P. Corbett.

Contents

Candle Lighting

From her place at the front of the platform, the director of the Center City Hospital School of Nursing smiled down at the crowd that overflowed the auditorium seats and stood along the back and sides of the hall. Strangers, most of them, yet she knew them all — the eager mothers so unashamedly proud; the fathers concealing their pride in carefully cultivated masculine offhandedness; the little sisters and brothers wriggling nervously, their voices rising now and again in high-pitched excitement, then falling suddenly as parental rebuke reminded them of the solemnity of the occasion. There, also, were the older sisters and brothers, whose determinedly bored faces could leave no doubt in anyone's mind that they were old hands at such ceremonies. And there, of course, was the scattering of really attentive young men whose interest, obviously, was anything but brotherly.

Yes, she knew them all. In the forty-odd years since she had received her own nurse's cap, she had seen them come and go, yet never without the secret thrill that a capping ceremony brought to her heart. The blasé young people in the audience would not be a fraction so bored, she told herself again, could they understand the inner meaning of the ceremony, the long bitter struggles and the hard-won triumphs implied. They no less than the students about to receive their caps, were the heirs of generations of nurses and of the noble traditions those nurses had built. Again, as always at such moments, she vowed that this night the audience would be made to understand a little.

As the hands of the clock in the rear of the auditorium clicked to eight, the director stood up. Slowly the bright lights were dimmed, bringing to gradual life the flame of the large candle that glowed on the table beside her. The organist struck the opening chords of the processional — proud notes for a proud ceremony. Then they entered, fifty girls in starched blue and white, looking very solemn despite their fresh youthfulness, carrying themselves with the self-conscious pride of those who are aware of having passed one of life's great milestones — having successfully completed six months' preclinical studies and now to be officially accepted as candidates for the nurse's diploma.

As the last girl moved into place, the director gestured faintly and the organist brought the march to a close. At another gesture, the girls were seated.

The director moved forward and began to speak, welcoming the students and their families. The audience glanced furtively at their programs. This must be the "Welcome." There would be a soprano solo, then the superintendent of the hospital would add his word of greeting. Then another solo. Then, at last, the moment for which all were waiting. But they were patient — all save the little brothers and sisters, that is — for such a moment as this must be approached without indecent haste.

At long last, the director introduced a tall, handsome woman in white — a school alumna and now a member of the school faculty — who approached the lectern and began to read from the manuscript resting there:

"In the beginning there was created heaven and earth and

all was in darkness . . ." she read in sonorous tones, re-counting briefly the ancient struggle between evil and good, between darkness and light. ". . . But always there have been men and women who kept alive the flame of knowledge and truth . . ." She made a gesture towards the candle flame, which seemed to take on a new brilliance.

". . . War and famine and pestilence," she read on, "have swept over the nations uncounted times, leaving in their wake death and despair. Today, even with wars all around us, we cannot quite grasp the horror of these words. For people have been given new hope and life a new dignity because a scant hundred years ago one woman, Florence Nightingale, set all her powers against the violence of war and the darkness of de-spair. With her nation in the midst of a bitter struggle, she led a group of women to nurse in army field hospitals . . ."

"Army field hospitals!" the director thought, "in the year 1854!"

What could this convey to people living in the present year of grace? How could any of those assembled here begin to com-prehend the utter filth and degradation of that terrible hospital in Scutari? How could they believe that more soldiers died of diseases contracted there than of the wounds which sent them from the battlefields? Or, grasping this, could they believe that one small, frail, gently bred lady had really, against blind and heated opposition, fought it all until she won through to vic-tory?

Today people saw only a disembodied, legendary figure holding a lamp far too small to throw out much of a light. Yet it was the flesh and blood woman, bowed with discouragement and fatigue, who walked the great barracks wards at night, carrying a lantern which she would set down as she leaned over the wakeful and suffering men. To those men, that lamp must indeed have seemed a bright beacon. So also must it have been to their families and to their nation, and soon to all the civilized world.

Across a wide ocean, an American named Longfellow was stirred to enthusiastic exclamation:

> Honor to those whose words or deeds
> Thus help us in our daily needs,
>   And by their overflow
>   Raise us from what is low!
>
> Thus thought I, as by night I read
> Of the great army of the dead,
>   The trenches cold and damp,
>   The starved and frozen camp, —
>
> The wounded from the battle-plain,
> In dreary hospitals of pain,
>   The cheerless corridors,
>   The cold and stony floors.
>
> Lo! In that house of misery
> A lady with a lamp I see
>   Pass through the glimmering gloom,
>   And flit from room to room.

Some people, the director thought as those lines ran through her head, said this was not great poetry. To her it would always be of the greatest, for the deeds were magnificent. Could anyone really find words to describe it all adequately?

Surely she herself had not found them, she thought, as she listened to the reading of the manuscript she had prepared with so much care, telling once more of that hospital at Scutari and of the grateful people in England who provided Florence with sufficient funds for her to realize her life's dream of founding the first modern school of nursing — a school which was to set an example to all peoples everywhere.

". . . And so tonight," the reader continued, "because she kept alive the light of knowledge and of truth — from this flame, symbolic of man's search for the highest and best, we light a candle in honor of Florence Nightingale."

The reader paused. The director picked up from the table a tall candle, lit it, and set it upright to add the glow of its flame to that already burning.

The reader began again, telling briefly of the history of her own school, of the farseeing and courageous women whose work had contributed to its founding and its growth. After each name she paused while a member of the school faculty rose and lit a memorial candle.

". . . Today," the reader went on when only one tall candle remained unlit, "we relight a candle for our school as a token that we renew our pledge to keep the flame burning brightly, so that our school may grow strong in the fight against all evil forces that bring disaster and disease . . ."

Together the elderly director and the young president of the student body reached for the last candle, lit it, and set it up beside the rest. Eight tall candles recording the history of their profession in living flame! In front were rows of smaller candles, still to be lit.

An expectant hush descended upon the whole auditorium while, with a fine sense of the dramatic, the reader thoughtfully and quietly regarded the row of flickering flames.

"And now," she read, "each student of this new class will light a candle from the flame of this our school candle, as a symbol of her acceptance of the traditions, the ideals, and the deep obligations of our school and our profession."

One by one, she called out the students' names. Each girl

in turn stood up, mounted the platform, and lit a candle that was thrust into her hands. Then, this symbolic act of dedication completed, she turned to face the director, who placed upon her head a stiffly starched nurse's cap. The rows of unlit candles slowly diminished while each of the fifty girls went through the ceremony and walked proudly down to stand facing the audience — her shimmering white cap a modern halo, her burning candle an altar flame. When the last girl had taken her place, the audience rose and all bowed their heads for the closing prayer and benediction.

Slowly the auditorium lights brightened. The organist struck up the notes of the recessional. Again the director surveyed the audience, briefly hushed and still, parents furtively wiping away tears of emotion, bored young faces obviously finding it hard to maintain a mature calm.

For a few brief moments perhaps, they had all shared her vision, seen the great and noble procession of which these proud young women were now becoming a part. If only, she thought, one could always hold such moments of exaltation — could remember that even in the midst of the hardest and most unpleasant tasks one was not alone, that many had walked that way before and many more would in the years to come, lighting candles in the midst of darkness until all the flames burning together would bring in a new day.

Part One
HERITAGE

CHAPTER I

Since the Days of Chivalry

These are exciting times for girls to be growing up. Even though there is still far too much cruelty and oppression in the world, even though kindness and brotherly love as well as the four freedoms seem to have a constant struggle against bitter odds, it is still a good world for the girl who finds a challenge in the work of her choosing and asks no more of the world than a chance to make something interesting and worth while of her life.

It has not always been so. It used to be — in those renowned days of chivalry — that a girl had to sit meekly in the house of some man, her father or brother, or a husband of her family's choosing, as shielded from the world as if she lived within the walls of a prison. While the menfolk went off to war and adventure in distant lands, the women and girls waited in great draughty castles or narrow, dark houses, filling the long, empty hours with embroidery or weaving or countless routine household duties. It might be years before their menfolk would return. It might be never.

One can well imagine that even those girls — who, after all, came from the same bold adventurous stock as the men and had in addition plenty of time for thinking things over — must have had many rebellious thoughts. Even though they had been carefully trained to obey their menfolk meekly and to wait unquestioningly and with endless patience for their knights' return, there must have been those who asked themselves — quite secretly, of course — Why?

Why was it that men were always faring forth to battle and adventure? Why was it that women always stayed behind? Why was it that women were expected to know how to deal with the world that found its way into their castles but were not fit to face the same world outside the castle walls? Why was it that men maimed and killed one another with such useless violence? Was there nothing women could do about it? Or could there be something?

A girl who rebelled too bitterly against her life at home might become a nun, exchanging one set of walls for another. The high-spirited and idealistic who perceived the poverty and hunger and sickness and death that rode the crooked streets in the wake of the knights, might feel a personal need to do something about it. To these, the best and, in general, the only way was to join some religious community whose avowed aim was to clothe the poor, feed the hungry, nurse the sick, and — alas, too often! — pray for the dying.

Now and again there was some great exception to this rule. Some wealthy and noble lady would feel a deep compassion for the misery about her and find that her compassion gave her courage. Though her actions would shock both friends and family, she might take upon herself a life of service to the poor and the sick.

Such a one was Princess Elizabeth of Hungary. Born in the year 1207, she was married at fifteen to a knight who, when she was only twenty and the mother of four children, set forth upon one of the Crusades, from which he was never to return alive. Until death claimed her at the ripe age of twenty-four, the noble widow filled her life with good deeds and spent much of the fortune left by her husband in aiding the poor and in relieving their suffering.

Should we light a candle for Princess Elizabeth? Not as a nurse — unless we are to light candles for all women of all ages who had high character and deep compassion. Noble though she was — and sainted though she now may be — she was not a nurse in our present sense. Centuries were to pass before such a type emerged.

The modern nurse must have a trained intelligence as well as high character, she must have fine personal discipline as well as deep compassion. Whether she remains at the bedside of her patients, ministering directly to the sick, or takes on the arduous duties of administration such as any large school or nursing organization requires, she is first and foremost the member of a profession, demanding as well as rewarding, of proud tradition. This tradition, born in the hospitals of the Crimean War, was nearly fifteen years old before it received due recognition on our side of the ocean.

It was in May of 1869, in the city of New Orleans, that the American Medical Association held a meeting to which Dr. Samuel David Gross sent a paper entitled "Remarks on the Training of Nurses." Dr. Gross wrote:

The establishment of schools for the education of nurses for private and public purposes, is a desideratum which has long been keenly felt in this country, both by the medical profession and by people at large . . .

. . . It is perhaps fortunate that the mortality occasioned by bad nursing cannot be properly estimated by those more immediately affected by it, as a knowledge of it would entail upon them an immeasurable amount of misery and mental anguish . . .

Dr. Gross's paper was long and persuasive, the first of its kind ever to appear in the United States. When so eminent a surgeon urged so radical an idea as that "every well-organized hospital should have a school for the training of nurses," other doctors could not toss it aside as the raving of an uninformed ignoramus.

Meanwhile women were making their own mark in the medical profession, but with the reluctant consent of men — so reluctant, in fact, that women doctors found it necessary to establish their own schools and hospitals to assure themselves, and those of their sex who were to come after, proper medical training and experience. The New England Hospital for Women and Children in Boston was one of these.

Susan Dimock, a beautiful young lady from the South, studied medicine in that hospital for two years, then went abroad to the University of Zurich in Switzerland, where, in 1871, she was graduated in medicine. At the age of twenty-four, she returned to the New England Hospital to become the first woman surgeon in America and one of the doctors who made possible here the first good hospital training of nurses. She was the founder of that first training school and its director until her untimely death by drowning four years later.

The annual report of the New England Hospital for 1871 –

1872 states: "In order more fully to carry out our purpose of fitting women thoroughly for the profession of nursing, we have made the following arrangements: young women of suitable acquirements and character will be admitted to the hospital as school nurses for one year . . ." At long last nursing was to become a "profession." In those days, one full year of training seemed ambitiously long, even though it was to be divided into four equal periods, in which the students would be rotated among medical, surgical, maternity, and night services. In addition to practical work, they would receive a total of twelve lectures given by the various women doctors of the staff. After the first fortnight of training, these students could expect to be paid for their work to the tune of one to four dollars a week, "according to the value of their actual services" — whatever that might mean. Their year would be crowned by a certificate of achievement.

Today this all sounds rather elementary, but for those days such training was advanced well beyond any other then available in the United States. As at the Nightingale school in England, applicants had to be carefully screened — no more than six young women being considered acceptable for the first American class. Of these, one soon became sick and was forced to leave, but five remained to graduate. The first to enroll, and consequently the first to receive her certificate, was the woman now frequently referred to as "America's first trained nurse" — Linda Richards.

Fortunately for those who have come after, Linda Richards wrote and published her reminiscences. It is a modest and all too short book which, to the mind of anyone interested in the progress of nursing, leaves many questions still unanswered. Nonetheless, it is a book which anyone so interested should read in its entirety, for Miss Richards's lifetime bridged the gap between the hit-or-miss nursing at the end of the Civil War and the highly organized and trained profession it has now become. In her training she eventually included the best both America and Great Britain had to offer and took her experience abroad to mission hospitals in Japan, where she helped found nursing schools for Japanese women. In active work until 1911 — living until 1930 — she saw modern nursing born and watched it come of age.

The years of her adolescence and young ladyhood were, like those of girls today, shadowed by wars. Born in 1841, Linda Richards was already, at the start of the Civil War, a grown young lady, though definitely far too young to be acceptable in army hospitals. During her early teens, war had broken out in the Crimea. Hazy and distant though this place may have seemed to a young American girl during the 1850's, it is hardly possible that she did not hear of Florence Nightingale's exploits there nor of the hope Miss Nightingale's skilled and organized nursing brought to so many men otherwise condemned to die.

Certainly during these years Florence Nightingale's life must have first reached out to touch hers — as it was to touch the lives of all modern nurses in all lands. Every story of modern nursing must begin with Florence Nightingale.

CHAPTER II

Florence Nightingale

What was there about Florence Nightingale that set her so far apart from other women? Wherein lies the special quality of her greatness? Why do so many nurses in America — even those who cannot unreservedly praise all she did — still place her first in the ranks of nurses?

To answer this, we must understand first of all that she was not a saint but a very real and human person — beautiful, wealthy, socially successful and enjoying this success during much of her youth. We must also understand that she cast these advantages aside with some reluctance and against the bitter opposition of family and friends, who were certain she was disgracing them. She chose a life of harrowing work and bitter frustrations. And though she accomplished much, she was always convinced that she had failed or fallen miserably short of the high goal she had set herself.

Perhaps just in this lies the secret of her greatness. Perhaps it is not the qualities whose sum makes up an individual, but rather that individual's imaginative choice of a goal — so high that he must spend all his life reaching for it — that constitutes the difference between an ordinary life and one that is in itself a lamp to cast its glow down through the ages.

Though the qualities we associate with Florence Nightingale are neither her high social standing, nor her wealth, nor her great personal charm, without these she could not have had the influence she had. Never at any time was she to receive personal financial reward from the country she served so long and loyally. But being a lady in the strictest Victorian sense — and a very strict sense this was — she probably would have regarded the offer of remuneration as something of an insult. Its acceptance might well have spelled the end of her influence upon those whose esteem and co-operation she needed. Hampered everywhere she turned by the limitations of a Victorian lady's life, she managed in the end to turn them into assets. Surely in any environment she must have been great.

The little girl Florence, named after the Italian city of her birth, and her slightly older sister Parthenope — Parthe for short — grew up in that protected Victorian atmosphere of ease and luxury and security which all prosperous Britons enjoyed after Napoleon was finally defeated by the British general Wellington. When Florence was a year old, the little family returned to England to live in a newly built home in Derbyshire in the north-central part of England.

Presently they added to this a large home in Hampshire on the south coast because — as the Nightingales quite seriously explained — the northern manor, Lea Hurst by name, had no more than fifteen bedrooms. Not, of course, that the family needed more than fifteen bedrooms to sleep in. Those were days without telephones or automobiles and with plenty of servants, when friends and relatives expected to visit back and forth in great numbers and, having undergone the inconvenience of travel in horse-drawn coaches on rough roads, to settle down for periods of rest and relaxation. With fifteen bedrooms frequently filled to overflowing, social life could never have been dull.

The mind of the modern householder is staggered by the cost of this way of life. Not so with Mr. Nightingale, who had inherited a fortune large enough to enable him to do as he wished without need to earn a living.

Presently he undertook the instruction of his small daughters in subjects he thought proper — mainly languages and history, which Florence loved and learned easily and Parthe soon found boring. Mrs. Nightingale, whose ideas on what a young lady should learn were quite different from her husband's, was on Parthe's side. Soon Parthe gave up the lessons altogether and delighted her mother's heart by performing a young lady's true duties. She arranged flowers, served tea, entertained guests or made visits herself, and wrote the innumerable notes and invitations necessary for a socially minded family in an era without telephones.

Parthe loved this kind of life. Florence, who at sixteen had to assume her share of these duties, thought it foolish and trivial. Were there still in the air echoes of those great revolutions of the century before — the American and the French — when the high were brought low and the low exalted and no matter where you lived your life was touched by great issues? Whatever the reason, there was within Florence a growing tension and a sense of guilt as she found that part of her enjoyed this trivial society. All her life she was to be torn between such opposing influences.

When she was seventeen, her parents decided upon yet another European tour. Slim, graceful, vivacious, her real beauty of feature accentuated by thick, glossy, golden-red hair, Florence soon became the center of any social group the Nightingales entered. Delighting in all this, she still cherished her dream of a personal dedication and was to find this dream supported by people she met far from the gay ballroom where she danced the old year out.

In Italy, she learned firsthand of the struggle to set the land free from Austrian domination. Years later this struggle was to culminate in the Battle of Solferino, where, fired by one Florence Nightingale's recent exploits, a Swiss gentleman named Henri Dunant would bring succor to the wounded and lay the foundations of a great international relief organization. More than twenty years were to pass before this would take place — years that would transform Florence from a brilliant and beautiful girl to a famous, idolized woman.

But this was the year 1837, when Geneva, Dunant's home, was the refuge of those Italians who, because of the active part they had already taken in the cause of freedom, were now exiles from their native land. To the gay young Englishwoman, these displaced persons afforded an entirely new experience. Intellectual, serious, bitterly poor, entirely without self-interest — they were as unlike the people of her set as could be imagined. Their example must have added weight to her secret conviction that a good life must be one of dedicated service.

Curiously enough, Florence did not have then, nor for some time to come, any idea what kind of service she should devote herself to. Nowadays any girl with such a conviction would surely consider nursing almost first among the possibilities. But in those days nursing was not a respectable profession — in fact it was hardly a profession at all. And little wonder, considering the kinds of women who, for the most part, became nurses and the kinds of places they had to nurse in.

In the 1840's, hospitals on both sides of the Atlantic were gloomy, overcrowded, incredibly dirty places where fifty or sixty beds were crowded into each clammily cold, unventilated ward. Ceilings, walls, and floors were practically never washed, and beds were so filthy that the odors of such hospitals caused nausea in most who entered for the first time. At least as many patients sickened there of new diseases as were, by some miracle, cured of those they had upon admission.

In fact, the only people who would consent to enter these institutions as patients were those who had no choice or who came from slums where conditions were as bad or worse. They did not expect to be washed — probably would have been outraged at the idea. Even hard and dirty beds may have been a luxury to them. Hospital rules against liquor caused them no annoyance for they always managed to get as much as they wanted anyway — and this was a good deal. In their drunkenness they added degradation to the dirt and disease.

In these pestholes, the women who nursed were rarely better than their patients. Most of them were also dirty and drunken. Many had prison records or vices that should have made them candidates for jail. All were ignorant and untrained in anything that would nowadays be called nursing technique.

It is not too surprising, then, that both Mrs. Nightingale and Parthe had hysterics when, in the year 1845, another Nightingale announced that she intended to learn something about nursing by working in the Salisbury Infirmary near Embley Park, the Nightingales' southern estate. Though the chief surgeon of the infirmary was a family friend, the place still was a hospital, and a young gentlewoman could bring only shame and disgrace upon her family by going to work in it. Florence, they were sure, was subjecting them to one of her fantastic and selfish whims.

This was, however, no passing whim. Florence had thought it all out carefully. Caring for the sick in her own family and among neighbors had given her a deeper satisfaction than anything else she had ever undertaken. But caring for them had also shown her how little she really knew about sickness. In the infirmary she thought to enlarge her experience and to gain a better understanding of nursing care. She saw no reason why nursing should continue to be a profession of ill repute. Surely all sick people needed the ministrations of specially trained and skilled women. But there were no such women to be had. This was a lack she was resolutely determined to remedy first by training herself.

Florence's family determined otherwise. They positively and violently forbade her entering the infirmary — and those were not days when daughters even as much as twenty-five years of age dared defy their parents. Outwardly she complied with their orders but inwardly her dream flourished. She began to collect reports on public health and hospitals — in so far as they were available in those days — both at home and abroad, keeping thus a secret contact with the matters that most interested her. Every day she arose very early to study while the rest of the household slept, so that her mother might not tearfully rebuke her for her indecent interest. As she read, she kept the carefully detailed notes that were one day to make her the first and foremost expert on public health in Europe.

Meanwhile her home duties and social life went on uninterruptedly. Admired by all, Florence was particularly sought by one very handsome and devoted and eligible young man whom later she referred to as "the man I adored." Yet she never married.

Perhaps if her family had permitted her to follow her own interests a bit more, she would not have felt so frustrated and unhappy, hating the life she had to live and all it forced her to endure. Perhaps if she had not hated it so, she might have married — and Florence Nightingale would have turned into Mrs. Monckton Milnes, just another beautiful and gay Victorian hostess who presided over her husband's manor and raised her husband's children and entertained her husband's friends, keeping correctly to the paths prescribed for Victorian ladies. Perhaps — who knows?

But when, in 1849, after nine patient years of paying court, Richard Monckton Milnes finally demanded an answer, she said "No" and lost him forever. Even so, she may have hoped he would return and persuade her that he would share her destiny just as she, the Victorian woman, must share her husband's. But he accepted her verdict and the loss was to make her far unhappier than she could have anticipated.

Meanwhile Florence's narrow world was expanding. On a recent trip abroad she had made some important new friends, among them one Sidney Herbert and his charming wife Liz, who were to have tremendous importance in shaping her life. Mr. Herbert, already influential in government circles, was a man with a social conscience that was to commit him to a life of dedicated service and to a too early death. He and his wife introduced Florence to a group of people who were becoming actively interested in hospital reform and among whom Florence's years of secret study at last proved their value. In her easy discussion of these matters, all recognized and acknowledged an expert.

It may be that this interest and the respect her opinions aroused in these important people gave Florence courage to revive her old determination to train for nursing. In 1851, against bitter family opposition, again carried to the point of hysterics on her mother's and Parthe's side, she went to an institution run by Lutheran deaconesses at Kaiserswerth, Germany. With all its faults — its overemphasis on menial work, its killing hours, and its rather too limited nurses' training — this place was the best available in those days. Nearly twenty years later, it was to be visited by the young American Dr. Susan Dimock, who would take home what she had learned and adapt it to the nursing school at the New England Hospital for Women and Children.

Once more settled in England, Florence was offered an opportunity to take charge of a nursing home with the impressive name Institution for the Care of Sick Gentlewomen in Distressed Circumstances. Certainly a place of respectability, anyone in our day would think. Not so Florence's family. Her mother once more raged and wept, and her sister worked herself into one of her hysterical frenzies. Poor Mr. Nightingale escaped it all by going to his club.

Most people today find it hard to understand why a terrible family crisis should result from a thirty-three-year-old daughter's taking upon herself the direction of such a worthy institution. This was to be an act of pure charity. Not only was she to receive no remuneration, she had to agree to hire at her own expense a matron who would be the sort of chaperon certainly required by anyone so youthful in appearance as she. But even the presence of this respectable person could not make such employment acceptable to Victorian society.

Nevertheless Florence persisted in her determination and became a most efficient administrator of the home. Her interest in hospital nursing and hospital reform continued, and, as she found time, she visited hospitals, made notes, collected information, and wrote reports about it all to Sidney Herbert, now an important cabinet minister. This was soon to lead her into far wider fields of action and into an unforgettable place in history.

Britain was at war in the Crimea — a peninsula jutting out into the Black Sea from the southern part of Russia, on whose shores the now famous Yalta lies. If you take the time to look it up, you may find a paragraph or so about the Crimean War — and will close your history book hardly wiser than when you opened it. Russia, it seems, started a quarrel with Turkey in a matter which the Turks felt concerned their national sovereignty. Fateful word! Then Britain joined in to help Turkey, largely to prevent a Russian victory and consequent Russian domination over the sea route to India. Ninety years later Britain and Russia were uneasy allies conferring at Yalta. Looking back across the years, we see British and Russian soldiers in 1854 dying with blind bravery less from each others' bullets than from common disease and inadequate care.

As always in wars, the warriors on either side expected an easy victory. So it was to be eight years later in our own Civil War. But in 1854, the British had the added delusion of believing their army to be the same which had, in 1815, defeated the superman of Europe, Napoleon Bonaparte. The British people were confidently awaiting a quick victory.

This was, unfortunately, not only another army, it was another war. It was the first in history to know field correspondents, and when one of them sent home a dispatch describing the horrible and unnecessary sufferings of the troops, the shocked nation rose up and demanded action. ". . . no sufficient preparations have been made for the care of the wounded," the correspondent wrote in part. "Not only are there not sufficient surgeons . . . not only are there no dressers and nurses . . . there is not even linen to make bandages . . . there is no preparation for the commonest surgical operations!"

Sidney Herbert, now Secretary at War, was the person from whom both the British public and his own private conscience demanded action. He was in a position to see to it that something was done, and fortunately — almost miraculously — he had someone to turn to.

On October 15, 1854, he wrote at length to Florence Nightingale, telling her as much as he personally knew of the conditions in the hospital situated at Scutari on the Asiatic shore of the Bosphorus. He went on to describe the enthusiastically patriotic ladies who were now volunteering for work in the hospital without having the slightest idea as to what hospital work really was and what special horrors they might expect to encounter in any military hospital during wartime. Finally, he came to the point:

. . . My question simply is, would you listen to the request to go and superintend the whole thing? You would, of course, have fullest authority over all the nurses, and I think I could secure you the fullest assistance and co-operation of the medical staff, and you would also have unlimited power of drawing on the Government for whatever you thought requisite for the success of your mission . . .

I do not say one word to press you . . . I must not conceal from you that I think upon your decision will depend the ultimate success or failure of the plan. Your own personal qualities, your knowledge and your power of administration, and among greater things your rank and position in Society give you advantages in such work which no other person possesses.

Florence, who had just sent off a letter offering her services, received the request on a Saturday. She immediately gave her consent and on Monday was appointed "Superintendent of the Female Nursing Establishment of the English General Hospitals in Turkey." Not only was she at last to superintend nurses, but she was to superintend them in the kind of hospital that had, before, known only men. The time for hysterics was past. Even the strictest of Victorians could find nothing but praise for such patriotic devotion.

Assisted by friends, Florence made a swift survey of the available professional nurses of good character and with sufficient hospital experience to make them useful. The sad condition of nursing in those days is underlined by the fact that they could find no more than fourteen. The rest of the forty Sidney Herbert had wished Florence to take with her had to come from religious bodies — Lutheran deaconesses, Roman Catholic nuns, and Anglicans. By October 21 — just one week after Sidney Herbert had sent his letter — nurses had been selected, uniforms ordered and completed, tickets purchased, reservations made, and the whole party prepared to leave on its mission.

On November 3, their ship dropped anchor off Constantinople, the present-day Istanbul, and the party of nurses, exhausted by a rough passage in a dirty ship and by the accompanying seasickness, could look from the great city on the northern side of the Straits to the huge barracks hospital building high on the Asiatic shore. From the ship, it seemed attractive.

But as they were brought close to shore, the nurses found they had to step out into mud made filthier by the unspeakable refuse that littered it. Packs of howling dogs were pouncing upon the bodies of dead animals left there to decay. It must have taken real stamina for the newly arrived women to land and pick their way up the steep, repulsive slopes. It must have taken courage to enter the hospital building and take up their abode there.

Bad as it was for these women, how much worse must it have been for the thousands of wounded and sick who had been carried or dragged up that horrible slope, through that same gate, to be laid in stinking, slimy-walled wards. Of these men, over half would be carried out again to rest forever in a foreign land. They would be killed less by their wounds than by the filth, and accompanying contagion, of the place and the lack of any decent care or sanitation. To change such conditions was to be not only Florence Nightingale's immediate problem but — so it eventually proved — her lifelong struggle.

The officers in charge of the hospital received the party of nurses with an outward show of courtesy. But the apparent warmth of the reception could do little to lighten the chilling effect of the quarters assigned them — six rooms, one a kitchen and one a large closet, for forty women. The rooms were hardly less damp and dirty than the rest of the hospital was to prove, and quite as penetratingly cold. There was practically no furniture and neither food nor light had been provided. Cold, hungry, and in darkness, the nurses finally found their way to bed.

It was not altogether accidental that those quarters were so discouraging to the high hopes with which the party of nurses had undertaken the venture. Hardly anyone in Scutari at that time — except possibly the sick men, who didn't seem to count — would have been saddened had that group of women decided the situation was more than they could be expected to endure. No one would have tried to keep them from taking the next boat home.

To the pleasure-loving British Ambassador and his lady, they were an embarrassment which sooner or later would probably involve troublesome responsibilities. Polite and suave though he was to their faces, he would not have been sorry to see them go.

Overworked and undersupplied, the doctors should have welcomed the group of women come to help ease their heavy labors. But women nurses were of doubtful repute anywhere and entirely unheard-of in army field hospitals. The surgeons knew, of course, that Florence Nightingale was a lady, but this did not help matters. They knew her social position to be above their own, her personal fortune large, and her backers powerful figures in British political life. To top it all, she had been entrusted with funds which she might spend without any reference to them — so that she appeared not so much a possible helper as a probable rival.

Women who, a few years later, were to enter field hospitals in our own land met similar suspicion and antagonism. Mary Phinney von Olnhausen, a Massachusetts woman, wrote of her first encounter, in the year 1862, with an army surgeon: "So I began my work, I might say night and day. The surgeon told me he had no room for me, and a nurse [male] told me he said he would make the house so hot for me I would not stay long . . ." Mrs. von Olnhausen did stay — without any quarters, working unceasingly, catching cat naps as she might and in whatever corner she could find a moment's refuge — until the surgeon was finally won over.

In any case, such attitudes could not persist, for the American women had one great advantage over their British sisters in the Crimea. In the Civil War, even field hospitals were relatively close to home and under the eyes of a people who had read dispatches from the Crimean War and knew how bad things might become if they were not vigilant. Mary Livermore, a writer of experience and a woman very active for the Sanitary Commission, remarks upon this: ". . . there was a resolute determination in the hearts of the people, that neither inexperience nor dogged adherence to routine should cause such wholesale slaughter of their beloved citizen soldiers." "Such slaughter" meant not that of the battlefield but such as occurred in the hospital at Scutari, and the "resolute determination" was thanks to the achievements of Florence Nightingale.

But Florence, newly arrived in the Crimea, could not foresee her eventual if hard-won triumph. Frustrated, but still not losing sight of her ultimate goal, she had to curb her impatience, resolutely shutting her eyes and ears to the crying needs of the wounded, and wait until by some personal request for help the surgeons might acknowledge her party as nurses. Then, on November 9, the combined effects of tough Russian soldiers and icy Russian winds brought a new flood of sick and wounded pouring into Scutari. More desperately overworked than ever, the surgeons were reluctantly forced to accept anyone who might give a helping hand.

Furthermore, in the midst of the tragic shortages by which they found themselves hampered, they suddenly recognized how providential it was that Miss Nightingale had funds that might be spent immediately without red tape or any higher authority than her own. Every day, in addition to working in and supervising the hospital, Florence made the boat trip across the Straits to the markets of Constantinople, where she purchased articles of which there was most urgent need. And the surgeons, their jealousies for the moment at rest, were grateful.

Today when we take hospital equipment and sanitation for granted, we find it hard to credit the tales of hospital conditions a mere century ago — that all these things could have been ignored until Florence took charge. In the markets she bought scrub brushes and rags as well as warm clothes, towels, soap, trays, screens — standard hospital equipment of our day but miserably lacking then. By the middle of December, hospital conditions in Scutari were so changed that the men who were carried from the dirty crowded hospital ships to be put in clean beds and fed warm nourishing food felt that they were being granted a glimpse of heaven.

Naturally, as they could, the grateful men wrote home about all this. And naturally their families talked. Without her knowledge or seeking, Florence Nightingale was becoming a public personage. The officers and surgeons, who felt they had worked quite as hard as she, were bitter about this acclaim. Again they spoke scornfully about her and would have undermined her if they could. But her power was so great that they had to respect it, if reluctantly, especially when the War Department set its seal of approval on her by reimbursing her for all the expenditures which she had made out of her own pocket.

Florence did not intend to give up before she was ready to go home, and that would be when the last patient was discharged. Her dearest hope was that in Scutari she might prove to the world the great value of women nurses in military hospitals. If they succeeded there, no hospital doors would again be closed to them and nursing might become a profession indeed.

Sadly, she found that not only army surgeons and red tape but the nurses themselves could be hampering influences. Many were splendid, but some complained bitterly and trivially about the unbecoming caps she expected them to wear. Some fretted about hospital shortcomings and wrote tactless letters that had unfortunate publicity at home — thus adding to Florence's troubles with the doctors. Some of the nurses deserted the work to marry men they met in the hospital. Occasionally her days were brightened by more humorous incidents, as when the agent of a wealthy Turk offered to buy from her a particularly plump young nurse who he thought might grace his master's harem.

For the most part, however, difficulties with nurses were due to the nineteenth-century woman's inability to subject her will to another woman's authority, to accept her orders without question, and to obey her instructions exactly. Later there were to be rivalries and bickerings among groups of different religious backgrounds who could not accept Florence as supreme. Only a person like Florence Nightingale — singleminded, just, courageous, self-forgetful — could have triumphed over the bitter frustrations all this implied.

Through it all, the sad procession continued. In January, 1855, there were only eleven thousand men encamped before Sevastopol in the Crimea, while the hospital at Scutari held twelve thousand with more coming in daily. When a new lot of sick and wounded were brought in, Florence might remain on duty for twenty-four hours at a stretch, completely disregarding any personal danger of contagion, seeing to it that the men were given clean clothes, decent beds, proper food. She nursed the most desperate cases herself and remained with the dying, for she made it her rule never to let a man die alone.

Though her labors increased almost hourly, she kept in sight the larger issues, making elaborate and detailed plans for complete reorganization of all hospitals. Her remarkable power to survey a huge problem without personal bitterness, to analyze it, to perceive the means of setting things right, was presently to make her a world authority in nursing and hospital administration and sanitation in general.

Somehow she found time to put her observations into lengthy letters which she sent to people who might take a hand in the reforms she dreamed of. She wrote late at night in cramped quarters where the roof was so bad that rain frequently came through it, puddled on the floor, then ran down into an officer's quarters beneath. He often claimed that "Miss Nightingale was pouring water on my head."

Save for the invalid diets she provided for the desperately sick, the hospital food was still almost uneatable. Each inmate of the hospital, herself included, was allowed only a pint of water a day for all needs. Ill fed, always exhausted, never able to find rest, she might work as much as eighteen hours out of the twenty-four. But she kept on.

Of course the men adored her. Her presence steadied them. Her own triumph over obvious fatigue made it easier for them to endure the pain they could not avoid. She cheered them through the long bleak days of convalescence. When they were well enough to write, they told about her to their loved ones at home.

Nurses also wrote. One who accompanied her on night rounds wrote home a description:

> . . . It seemed an endless walk . . . As we slowly passed along the silence was profound; very seldom did a moan or cry from those deeply suffering fall upon our ears. A dim light burned here and there. Miss Nightingale carried her lantern which she would set down before she bent over any of

the patients. I much admired her manner to the men — it was so tender and kind.

In England, people were talking more and more about Florence Nightingale. When news of her dangerous illness reached home, it brought sadness to thousands who had never seen her. Strangers stopped one another in the streets to inquire the latest news of her health, and when at last she was known to be convalescing there was general rejoicing. Though Florence had forbidden her family to give out her picture and though they — at last wakened to pride in her — respected her wishes, they could not stop people from trying to picture the person whom they so adored. From vague descriptions and out of their grateful imaginations, they drew their idealized portraits of the Lady with the Lamp.

Other people wanted to put their affection into more tangible form. Knowing that she had dreamed of founding a school for nurses, they collected money to go into a "Nightingale Fund" which she might later use to make of her dream a reality. Any other gift, these people knew, she would have rejected.

Still in the Crimea, as each emergency waned, Florence had to contend with the opposition and intrigues of medical officers. Yet she remained on duty until the war ended in 1856 in a British victory. Exhausted by her illnesses (for she had contracted the terrible dysentery as well as Crimean fever — now known as *typhus*) and by the aftereffects (sciatica, laryngitis, ear trouble), driven to incredible efforts by the demands of her work, tormented by spiteful persecutions, she somehow managed to carry on.

In the end, Florence went home sick and discouraged, convinced that all had ended in miserable failure. Not only her own grateful countrymen but future generations everywhere would see it differently. Almost singlehanded, she had raised nursing to the level of an honored profession.

The people of England were eagerly waiting to honor her both for her own achievements and for her so passionate espousal of the cause of their soldiers. But she refused everything. Those accustomed to the fantastic welcomes afforded modern heroes and heroines will find it hard to believe that after her return to England, Florence Nightingale never made a public appearance. She refused gifts, honors, and interviews and so shunned all publicity that within two years many assumed she had died.

Yet frail and wasted by disease and confident of an early death though she was, Florence lived to the age of ninety. For about fifty of those years she kept up a never flagging struggle with reluctant authorities to improve sanitary conditions both in army hospitals and army barracks. The thousands of soldiers she had left behind in Crimean graves haunted her and would not let her rest. They were always her first and most urgent responsibility.

They were not, however, her only responsibility. Always endowed with enough energy for several people, she managed to find time to write books such as *Notes on Hospitals* and *Notes on Nursing* — which latter soon reached the best-seller class. And finally, in 1859, Florence consented to use the Nightingale Fund to establish the first truly modern training school for nurses. Though her studies on sanitation and her unceasing efforts to persuade cabinet ministers and army authorities to accept her findings made it impossible for her to take full personal charge of such a school, she could draw up plans, select the hospital where the school should be situated, and even fight the school's battles.

After much consideration, Florence chose St. Thomas's Hospital in London. Already in charge there was a matron who she felt was properly equipped by intelligence and character — not by formal training, for one must remember there had been nothing of the sort available — to supervise the school. Most important, the matron was an English "gentlewoman." This meant that she came of a family of good social standing and had had a good education in terms of what was then available to women. It meant, further, that she knew how to behave with correctness and dignity and to keep the respect of all with whom she must deal — which was especially important in days when many were still inclined to question the respectability of anyone who went into nursing.

The name of this matron might have been chosen by her contemporary Charles Dickens, and Linda Richards's description of her as she appeared nearly twenty years later only adds to the impression that she stepped out of a Dickens novel:

> . . . On the following beautiful May morning, I presented myself at St. Thomas's, and was shown into the office of Mrs. Wardproper, the matron of the hospital. Seated before a desk was a small lady dressed in black. Upon her head was a cap of lace with long, flowing strings, which were not tied in front, but hung down her back nearly to her waist. Upon her hands were black kid gloves. During my stay at the hospital [nearly six months] I never saw her in any other dress. I think it was her uniform, and she was as much at home writing in gloves as is the ordinary individual without them. The few moments of my interview with Mrs. Wardproper served to impress upon my mind the remarkable characteristics which enabled her during her long years of service, to play so large a part in developing the usefulness of this great institution.

Obviously Florence Nightingale had made no mistake in selecting a place presided over by such a person. This was to be a school where nurses would be trained so that they might go out to found or supervise other schools and build up a tradition of fine nursing throughout the land — growing up, perhaps, into Mrs. Wardpropers?

The first probationers, of course, had to meet especially high standards of character and intelligence. Not until June, 1860, were fifteen of them found. The training — to last for the then incredibly long period of one year — was hard and the work heavy. Rules were so strict that, for instance, it was forbidden for any student nurse to appear on the street alone. Fortunately for so human a profession, the young women were not quite superhuman. One of them, reminiscing years later, remarked that although the girls might set out properly in twos or threes, they always separated promptly as soon as out of sight of the hospital.

Nevertheless, despite moments of rebellion, the chosen fifteen must have had great satisfaction in knowing themselves to be pioneers in new fields and followers, though at a distance, along paths Florence Nightingale had explored. In moments of discouragement or depression, they could always turn to her, finding there a real personal interest and friendship. As long as she lived, every girl who was to become a Nightingale nurse was known to her personally. And every good nurse, Nightingale or otherwise, looked up to her with worshipful admiration.

Whatever her preoccupations — and they were always many and weighty — Florence Nightingale usually managed to find time to see and talk with nurses. Visitors of fame and importance among her own countrymen, and others, were turned away. Neither the great Dorothea Dix nor Clara Barton ever penetrated her sanctum. But the American nurse Linda Richards, earnest but unacclaimed, coming to study in England, was given a cordial welcome. Linda's ecstatic description of this visit gives not only a picture of Florence Nightingale in 1877, but also may help to convey an idea of the unique place she held in the minds and hearts of American nurses as well as English and of the importance of her life in the history of American nursing:

> Miss Nightingale had from the first known all about my plans for visiting St. Thomas's Hospital, and had sent me a message of welcome soon after my arrival in England. It had never occurred to me that she would honor me by asking me to call upon her, so great was my surprise when I received an invitation to visit her at her home. I had been only four days at the hospital, and was as yet a stranger to English ways. Even now I can distinctly recall with what fear and trembling I walked toward the house of the woman who had for years been an inspiration to me and to countless others. Was it really I myself who was walking up the steps of her house? Was I really to behold Miss Nightingale's face, to look into her eyes, to hear her voice, to feel my hand clasped in hers? It seemed indeed too strange to be true.
>
> Before I hardly realized the fact, I found myself face to face with a small lady clad in black silk, lying upon a couch, for, as is well known, she had been an invalid for years. A small hand was held out to me, and a low, pleasant voice bade me, an American nurse, a cordial welcome to England and to her home. The sweet face, with the deep blue eyes, and the beautifully shaped head, I saw at a glance. The one dream of my nursing years was being fulfilled: I was indeed talking with the one woman whose name and the record of whose good works were known throughout the civilized world. I see her now as I write these words. Such consummations of our desires are never to be forgotten.
>
> .   .   .   .
>
> Many and varied blessings have come to me through the years of my hospital life, but never one greater than the

privilege of having seen and known Miss Nightingale . . .
What a work for suffering humanity has been accomplished
through her! What a beautiful and beneficent life hers has
been!

CHAPTER III

Civil War Nursing

Even though bitter wars were soon to be waged close by on the European Continent as well as far across the ocean, Florence Nightingale was never again to visit battlefields or move among the wounded in field hospitals. But the flame of her lamp did not go out. Others were to tend it and to carry it high as she had done. Humanity was no longer willing to take for granted the brutality and suffering and disease that accompanied war.

In the year 1859, war finally broke out between Italy and Austria. Forty thousand men, killed or wounded, lay on the battlefield in Northern Italy. Among these moved Henri Dunant; assisted by women from neighboring villages, he undertook the task of ministering to the sick and dying, who were to haunt him as the Crimean victims did Florence Nightingale. Recognizing that many might have been saved by timelier and more efficiently organized aid, he wrote a little book, *Un Souvenir de Solferino (Remembrance of Solferino)*, a milestone in civilization's progress. "Would it not," he asked, "be possible to found and organize in all civilized countries permanent societies of volunteers who in time of war could render succor to the wounded without distinction of nationality?"

It was, of course, possible. Anything is possible when high-minded and determined souls set to work. Within five years Dunant's eloquence had moved so many people that fourteen nations were willing to send representatives to a meeting called for the purpose of discussing and organizing a new international relief committee. They met in Geneva, Dunant's native city, under the peaceful Swiss flag on which a white cross glowed in a blood-red field. Out of respect for its founder and the place of its founding, the committee voted to take for its symbol the reverse of that flag — a red cross — and the organization was called the International Red Cross Committee.

To these proceedings, the American Minister to Switzerland came as unofficial representative. America was across an ocean that was, in effect if not in fact, wider than it is now. Isolated isolationist America never expected to be involved in international wars in which she would need the protection of such an organization. Though she might humanely applaud the idea back of the Treaty of Geneva, she could see no possible reason for taking a more active interest. To change this attitude would take many years of heartbreaking struggle on the part of one devoted, determined, single-minded American woman — a woman who first learned about war on the battlefields and in the hospitals of her own war-torn land.

In April, 1861, Fort Sumter was fired on and the North and South were at each other's throats. As with most wars, people had dreaded it beforehand but had not really expected it. It simply could not happen here. Any fool could see that if once started it must end in no more than three months — with victory, of course, in the hands of the side which happened to be talking. In other and now so familiar words, no one was prepared.

Unprepared, fired by devotion to the causes in which they believed, men of all ages and from all walks of life enlisted in the citizen armies. They knew what they were fighting about and were ready to die for it, if need be, on whatever battlefield fate might choose. But as in the Crimea, fate did not always choose a battlefield.

Army organization was as unprepared as the civilian volunteers. Though civilian doctors had volunteered along with their townsmen, army officers frequently felt that army surgeons should confine their services to wounded men or those sick with contagious diseases. With the germ theory of disease still a-borning, sanitation and camp inspection were newfangled ideas that irritated the always conservative army officers.

Dr. Alfred Castleman, attached to the Fifth Regiment of Wisconsin Volunteers, kept a diary telling of his troubles with superior officers. One of these issued an order forbidding him to interfere with camp sanitation. After three weeks of illness mounting to the point where the Wisconsin governor expressed his alarm, this order was finally rescinded.

A week later the doctor made the following eloquent entry: ". . . Eight days ago today, the sick list was 144. Today it is 72! I begin to think a Surgeon may be as indispensable to an army as a Colonel . . ."

Not all regiments were equally fortunate in their medical

staff. In November, 1861, at about the time Dr. Castleman was forbidden to interfere in sanitation, one young man who had enlisted during his sophomore year at college wrote home:

> I suppose you would like to hear what we are doing in Virginia in the way of bringing the rebels to subjection. As yet we have done little fighting but have lost a large number of men. They are dying daily in camps and hospitals, from pneumonia, dysentery, and camp diseases caused by severe colds, exposure, and lack of proper food when ill . . .
>
> Our hospitals are so bad that the men fight against being sent to them . . . If we could be sure of being halfway well cared for when we get sick or wounded, it would take immensely from the horrors of army life.
>
> We need beds and bedding, hospital clothing and sick diet, proper medicines, surgical instruments, and good nurses — and then a decent building or good hospital tent for the accommodation of our sick. I suppose we shall have them when the government can get around to it, in the meantime we try to be patient.

Letters like this went back home by the dozens, many finding their way into print in local newspapers. The men might try to be patient, but their womenfolk at home saw no reason to be. They intended to do something about it.

Almost immediately they formed, in New York, the Woman's Central Association of Relief. Under the guidance of a Congregational clergyman, Dr. Henry Bellows, this soon led to the development of the United States Sanitary Commission, patterned after the British Sanitary Commission of the Crimean War and possibly influenced in addition by Henri Dunant's writings. The commission refused government support, which might have involved government red tape. It refused also special authority to enforce its designs — the need of force being a confession of failure.

Dr. Castleman, who had once been so opposed to the commission as to let fellow surgeons persuade him to write condemning it, was finally won to boundless enthusiasm. His tribute describes an organization supported entirely by voluntary contributions, functioning without force through the consent of both officers and soldiers, assuming gradually most of the duties of relief on the battlefields and behind the lines, to the soldiers and to their families, that the Red Cross has undertaken in more recent wars.

Save for recognized hospital inspectors and field agents in charge of distributing commission supplies, the Sanitary Commission had little to do with the running of hospitals or with the nursing of the ill. According to the surgeon and, possibly, the matron in charge, a hospital might be excellent or terrible. If bad, it usually was so less through negligence than through inexperience and a lack of appreciation of what truly good nursing might accomplish. In those days the science of hospital administration as well as that of nursing had not yet been born.

The Nightingale school at St. Thomas's had yet to graduate its first class and there would be no graduate nurses in America for another twelve years. However, in the year 1861, Dr. Elizabeth Blackwell, the first woman medical graduate in America and a friend of Florence Nightingale's, tried to plan a month's training for women who were to nurse in army hospitals. Possibly it was because the idea of hospital training for women was so new and radical, possibly because civilian hospitals had such evil reputations, possibly because women believed they could nurse by instinct rather than by training — but in the rush of wartime needs even this modest plan failed and women went entirely untrained. Fortunately many women volunteers learned quickly as they went and did a remarkable job. Others proved utterly unfit for the harrowing work.

Women who romantically dreamed of themselves as new Florence Nightingales rushed into army nursing. Some were never officially appointed — just happened to turn up on a visit to some sick friend or relative at some moment of dire need, lent a helping hand, and found themselves urged to remain by the harassed surgeon. Some applied for official appointments when they got around to it. Some never got around to it. The thirteen-dollars-a-month compensation did not, even in those days, seem particularly alluring.

Many women volunteered in emotional excitement and, because the need was so great, were uncritically accepted. But they soon proved all too human. Some simply could not take it — and, to do them full justice, the work was far harder to take than most modern women can imagine. Some took it well but talked too much and stirred up trouble with the surgeons. Most of them were still convinced that though woman might be divinely ordained to smooth the fevered brow and comfort the departing soul, her place was definitely not in army hospitals. Some of the women were inefficient — crime enough in the midst of a bitter war. Some, alas! were downright dishonest and some — one may guess — vain and flirtatious.

Dr. Thomas T. Ellis, a post surgeon in New York, left in a diary published in 1863 a record of the problem of obtaining satisfactory nurses. He wrote: ". . . Women from New York and other cities, of doubtful age and reputation, had succeeded in getting employed as nurses . . ." Then he went on to describe the depredations these women inflicted upon suffering and helpless soldiers, and their embezzlement of supplies collected so laboriously by private individuals as well as by the Sanitary Commission.

One of the main troubles must have been that no one really

knew then what a nurse's duties should include. Their work varied widely from place to place. In the main, in hospitals remote from battlefields they administered medicines as directed by the surgeon in charge, dressed wounds if they knew how or could acquire the skill, aided orderlies in preparing meals, fed the more helpless patients, wrote letters for them, read or sang to them and played games with them if the patients wished. Nurses might also take charge of the hospital laundry — if any was done, supervise women hired for that work and, like everyone else connected with the army, prepare their own meals from raw food issued them.

Women who served in front lines did whatever the emergency required. Sometimes they not only cooked meals for the men over open campfires — they also had to forage for the materials to cook. Sometimes they fed the men whose wounds they had barely finished dressing. All too frequently they were called on to assist in the terribly common business of amputation — giving anesthetic if they knew how and if any were mercifully available. If it were not, they stood by, assisting as they could, biting their lips at the pain being inflicted and closing their eyes to the grim pile of severed limbs so recently throbbing with life. What they did not know of all this they learned the hard way as need arose.

As luck would have it, in the early days of the war there came to America one Dr. Muir, Medical Inspector General of the British army. Dr. Muir had had experience in the Crimea, so that after he toured the army hospitals in Virginia, the harassed surgeons there eagerly asked for his advice and listened respectfully to his suggestions, among which, as Dr. Ellis records, ". . . he advised the organizing, under a competent head, of the female nurses, who should be selected between the ages of thirty and forty-five . . ." Whatever the

Medical Inspector General may have thought when Florence Nightingale first arrived at Scutari, he must have ended up a wholehearted convert.

At last, after six months of hit-or-miss nursing service, the army acknowledged that some organization was necessary and persuaded Dorothea Dix, a woman widely known for her interest in mental hospitals, to take over the superintendency of nurses for all military hospitals. A circular issued shortly after described the type of woman the army surgeons — mindful undoubtedly of Dr. Muir's advice — felt desirable: "No woman under thirty need apply to serve in government hospitals. All nurses are required to be very plain-looking women. Their dresses must be brown or black, with no bows, no curls, no jewelry, and no hoop-skirts."

No one, of course, had then dreamed of the antiseptic purity of modern nurses' starched uniforms. In the best hospitals, even, surgeons were operating in their oldest and dirtiest coats, hanging them uncleaned in the operating rooms when each day's work was done. In discussing his medical education in the year 1880, Sir Wilfred Grenfell of Labrador fame describes a great British surgeon, clad in a bloodstained velvet coat, amputating a leg. Naturally the nurses of such an era would not have wished to risk spattering their best clothes with blood, but for some of them it was almost too much to be denied all trimmings.

It must, in any case, have taken singular modesty and self-denial for any woman to fit herself to the descripion in the circular issued by Miss Dix. Years later, Miss Mary Holland of Boston recorded her determination to serve her country and her mother's insistence that if she served it must be "under government protection." She described her own reluctance to respond to the call when faced with a final decision: "It was fashionable at that time to wear immense hoops. I had worn one for some time and really felt it a sacrifice to leave it off. Other requirements were agreeable but I felt I could not walk without a hoop."

As the horrors of war grew and multiplied and descriptions of the still worse plight of the wounded filled to overflowing all newspapers, Miss Holland decided she could survive, if need be, without a hoop. In a mood of sacrifice, she wrote Miss Dix: "I am in possession of one of your circulars and will comply with all your requirements. I am plain-looking enough to suit you, and old enough. I have no near relative in the war, no lover there. I never had a husband and am not looking for one. Will you take me?"

Miss Dix seems to have been delighted to have been offered the services of one so obviously well fitted to nurse in government hospitals. She replied promptly: "Report at once to my house, corner of 14th Street and New York Avenue, Washington."

Apparently, however, Miss Dix did not like her nurses' costumes to depart too far from women's conventional dress. Mrs. Amanda Farnham, a Vermont individualist who had served for two years without government appointment, finally in May, 1864, applied to Miss Dix for an official appointment as an army nurse. She appeared for the interview in a costume astonishing for any time. Her husband later described it: ". . . full pants buttoning over the tops of her boots, skirts falling a little below the knee, and a jacket with tight sleeves."

Miss Dix glanced over the papers Mrs. Farnham presented, then glanced over Mrs. Farnham. Mrs. Farnham began to flush under the scrutiny.

Then Miss Dix spoke curtly, "Mrs. Farnham, the dress you

wear is abominable — a most abominable dress — and I do not wish my nurses to dress in that manner."

But Mrs. Farnham was by now an expert nurse and came highly recommended at a time when experienced and willing nurses were needed. Whether she said anything in defense of her costume is not known. More likely she let her credentials speak for her.

Finally Miss Dix, who undoubtedly realized that if she took Mrs. Farnham she must also take Mrs. Farnham's costume, conceded, "I have long known of your work, but I didn't know you wore such a dress. However, you may wear it if you choose."

Mrs. Farnham did choose and continued to wear it throughout her government service, which ended in June, 1865. Though Miss Dix must have seen it and possibly shuddered at it many times, she never mentioned it again.

Many of the women volunteers gave long, hard, devoted service, often with serious damage to their own health. Hospital conditions could give loyal Americans little basis for shocked condescension over those at Scutari. Louisa May Alcott, presently to become the famous author of *Little Women,* who served briefly in a Washington hospital, described its impact upon her: "The first thing I met was a regiment of the vilest odors that ever assaulted the human nose . . . and the worst of this affliction was, every one assured me that it was a chronic weakness of all hospitals and I must bear it."

This was only part of what was borne by all such women — other writers and journalists, teachers who had left their schoolrooms and would later return there, women who were presently to become physicians in their own right, and others whose talents lay more directly and less spectacularly in the tending of the ill and the mothering of the lonely and suffering.

There are thick volumes, with that strange, musty smell found in books scarcely opened for over half a century, where one may see the engraved features and read the printed exploits of any number of onetime much-loved Civil War nurses. Most of these fine women are now forgotten. Theirs was a personal contribution — brave and courageous but, alas! no more enduring than the flesh and blood of those they nursed. The women whose names remain living to this day are those who saw beyond the turmoil of war to larger issues and greater public responsibility.

Possibly nothing could give a better understanding of nursing at the time of the Civil War than brief sketches of the lives of the four women here chosen. Two of them are women whose influence has lasted down the years and reached far beyond their own land — Dorothea Lynde Dix, most of whose life was devoted to the improvement of the horribly wretched lot of insane paupers; and Clara Barton, for much of the Civil War an independent agent bringing relief directly to the battlefields and learning thereby the lessons that would cause her to dedicate the rest of her life to the cause of the Red Cross. The third woman — though of some renown because of her picturesque saltiness — typifies the main body of now forgotten self-sacrificing women. This was Mary Ann Bickerdyke, a woman without wide vision but a marvelous housekeeper and cook who carried her highly developed domestic talent into hospitals where it was sorely needed. Fearless in defying on behalf of her "boys" the arbitrary authority of all those who seemed to be stuffed shirts, she made herself a terror to the unrighteous and a legend to those whose causes she espoused. The first three were Northerners, the fourth, Kate Cumming, a Southern lady and Confederate nurse.

CHAPTER IV

Dorothea Dix

Dorothea Lynde Dix was born in Maine in April, 1802. Her childhood seems to have been a very bleak and unhappy one, dominated by her father, an impoverished religious fanatic. In later life Dorothy was very reluctant to talk about her early years, but their wretchedness is shown by the fact that at the age of twelve she ran away to her grandmother in Boston.

A biography of Dorothea, written in 1896, describes the home to which she fled and the grandmother under whose care she placed herself. Madam Dix was very well off financially, her husband having been both physician and apothecary and a shrewd investor of earnings from both these sources. The biographer writes:

> Madam Dix was a typical example of the New England Puritan gentlewoman of the period, — dignified, precise, inflexibly conscientious, unimaginative, and without a trace of emotional glow and charm. . . . To Madam Dix, then, and to the old Dix mansion, the child Dorothea owed, on the one hand, a debt of lasting obligation and, on the other, years of acute suffering and heart starvation.

In later years, Dorothea was to cry out the bitter words, "I never knew a childhood!" Conscientiously and sternly, her grandmother prepared her to earn her way in the world in which she must live, giving her a good education and wasting no time before launching her upon a teaching career.

When only fourteen years old, the tall, beautiful, easily blushing girl lengthened her sleeves and skirts to command a respect she feared her obvious youth might deny her, and set forth to teach in a school for little children in Worcester, Massachusetts. As it turned out, discipline was never to be a problem to this girl who in her life had known almost nothing but discipline. Soon, however, it appeared that if she was to be the kind of teacher either she or her grandmother wished, she must take further training. So, at the end of the term, she returned to Boston to study until she reached the advanced age of nineteen.

Sometime during these years, Dorothea became engaged to marry a cousin. What happened to this engagement no one seems to know, but it came to an end and Dorothea added one more burden of unhappiness to a life that had already known too many. She was not, apparently, permanently embittered by her loss, for later in life it was always her romantic hope to bring together couples whom she thought particularly suited to one another.

The year 1821 saw Dorothea opening in her grandmother's mansion a school for girls of prosperous New England families. In a room over the stable, she also held classes for the city's poor and neglected children. No easy schedule this! By 1824, years of overwork and stern self-denial began to tell upon her; her self-discipline finally gave way and she collapsed in an attack of what must have been tuberculosis.

She needed rest and a warmer climate — both of which fate obligingly offered her. Dr. William Ellery Channing, an eminent minister for whom Dorothea had a hero-worshiping admiration, invited her to tutor his children in his summer home in Rhode Island and, later, during a stay on the tropical island of St. Croix. Here she enjoyed herself and built up her strength to the point that, in 1831, she thought herself well enough to undertake schoolteaching once more. But she had not learned her lesson. Again she overworked until, in 1836, hemorrhages and sharp pains in her side brought her low.

Without the strength to drive herself further, Dorothea had to give in to friends' urgings. She finally consented to take the trip abroad that in those days was usually prescribed for anyone in failing health and with the price of a passage. In England, she again collapsed and was nursed for eighteen months in the home of a gentleman to whom Dr. Channing had given her a letter of introduction.

This gentleman, Mr. William Rathbone of Liverpool, was the same who was later to beg Florence Nightingale's assistance in the setting up of a system of district nursing in his city. Could it be that so long residence in the home of this prosperous and philanthropic gentleman set Dorothea's mind in the direction it was to take so soon after her return to her own land?

By the time Dorothea returned to Boston in the summer of 1837, her grandmother had died, leaving her a bequest sufficiently large to relieve her of the driving need of supporting herself by her own labors. She was not, of course, a person who really knew how to take things easy. Something worth while she must be doing, and this something was soon offered to her, all unknowing, by a young theological student of Cambridge.

He had been asked to teach Sunday school in the East Cambridge jail. When he found himself facing a class of twenty women — the kinds of women who, undoubtedly, enjoyed making a young theological student uncomfortable — he decided they would surely be better off under a woman teacher. His mother suggested Miss Dix might advise him. Miss Dix, when approached, promptly replied, "I will take them myself."

"And thus," as the young man explained when he was no longer young and could view the tremendous consequences of this little episode, "I was simply the instrument of the Good Providence to open the door for this Angel of Mercy to come in."

It was natural that after her first class was finished, Miss Dix should decide to visit the jail. In the home of William Rathbone she must have heard spirited discussions of the conditions in hospitals and almshouses and jails of Liverpool. Perhaps she wanted to take this opportunity to find out if things were not better in her own land.

Dorothea's social conscience must have been profoundly shocked when she saw the conditions and realized that the helpless insane were housed with criminals, all herded together without stoves to warm them because it surely was not worth while wasting fuel on such scum. She saw the filth and over-crowding, saw that the treatment of insane paupers was little better than it had been in the Dark Ages, when insanity was thought to be produced by devils who had taken possession of and actually entered the bodies and minds of their victims. Though no one any longer believed that the way to cure in-sanity was to subject the insane to torture which might dis-courage and drive out those devils, people had not yet learned to treat the insane with the same compassion they would hold towards anyone whose illness was regarded as purely physical.

Was the situation in East Cambridge an exception or might it be the rule? Dorothea Dix determined to find out. Armed with notebook and pen, she traveled her state from the sea to the Berkshires, visiting one jail and almshouse after another, making carefully detailed notes of everything she saw. She observed with terrible impartiality and recorded accurately. At the end of two years, she addressed a memorial to the State legislature: "I proceed, gentlemen, briefly to call attention to the present state of insane paupers confined within this Com-monwealth, in cages, closets, cellars, stalls, pens; chained, na-ked, beaten with rods and lashed into obedience. . . ." She concluded the lengthy memorial with an impassioned appeal for better care for the insane — for the enlargement of existing asylums and for the building of new and better ones where, in pleasant, restful surroundings, those unfortunates might have a chance of regaining their sanity.

Naturally the memorial aroused a storm of protest. Miss Dix — so outraged officials claimed — was an ill-intentioned busy-body and publicity seeker. But Miss Dix had justice and mercy on her side. She also happened to have prominent and influential friends. The legislature finally had to give in and passed a bill providing for the more humane care of the insane in properly managed asylums. The quiet, careful, inflexibly just Miss Dix had won the first of a long series of victories.

Friends who knew Miss Dix at this time describe an exceptionally attractive person — wavy, dark brown hair, brilliant blue-gray eyes, brightly glowing cheeks. Her well-shaped head, graceful carriage, and quiet good taste in dress combined to lend her an air of unusual distinction. Perhaps most outstanding was the quality of her voice — sweet, rich, low, and, obviously, tremendously persuasive.

It was this voice that was to be raised in behalf of insane paupers all over the nation. Dorothea traveled from one state to another, collecting evidence with her usual painstaking care, memorializing legislatures, interviewing legislators and persuading them, often against their will, to introduce and pass the necessary bills. North, South, East, West — everywhere they fell under the spell of her personality and her voice, raised — as Florence Nightingale's was presently to be — in behalf of those who could not raise their voices for themselves.

It is interesting to compare these two so famous women. Their backgrounds were about as widely divergent as possible — Florence belonging to a society at once luxurious and trivial where emotions ran riot in hysterics and fainting fits; Dorothea born into poverty, her emotions sternly disciplined from childhood; Florence yearning for a career and long denied one, whereas Dorothea was expected to choose hers at the early age of fourteen. Both of these women were exceptionally attractive, both were to move with ease among the highest statesmen, bringing to bear powerful influences for the groups of unfortunates they chose to champion.

Dorothea was at work on behalf of the insane long before Florence went to the Crimea. While Florence was there, friends again persuaded Dorothea to take a sea trip, hoping it might bring her sorely needed rest. But this time she would not rest. Single-minded — and on her own initiative — she set to work for the insane in Scotland and the Channel Islands, and then toured Europe, where she visited not historical monuments but insane asylums. An unflinching Unitarian, she did not hesitate to pay her respects to the Pope so that she might call his attention to abuses in the care of the insane under his jurisdiction. He listened to her gravely, investigated her reports and found them just, and, thanking her for her interest, assured her the abuses would be corrected.

Like Florence Nightingale, Dorothea Dix seems to have had an unusually clear analytical intellect. With careful thoroughness she studied the field in which she interested herself, learned how things should be, how to recognize promptly where things were otherwise and how to set them right. She had the same ability to bring order out of a chaos of apparently unrelated facts and to impress statesmen with her extraordinary intellectual capacity, her spiritual drive, and her utter personal integrity.

How, had they met, would these two strong-willed women have felt toward one another? Certainly Dorothea admired Florence immensely for her exploits in the Crimean War, and went out of her way to try to call upon Miss Nightingale in Scutari. Her comments upon the hospital at that date — written in a letter to Mrs. Rathbone — present an interesting picture of the order the Englishwoman had brought there:

. . . I paid and discharged the boatmen, and, inquiring of an English sailor the way to the nurse's quarter, proceeded thither. Miss Nightingale was absent, having been a month at

Balaklava, where there is much sickness of the English and French troops. I went over the chief hospital, which was in excellent order, and chiefly filled with convalescents . . .

If Dorothea said it was in excellent order, one may be quite sure it was in excellent order. Dorothea's eyes were well trained to detect disorder. However, she was never to have the privilege of expressing her approval to Florence Nightingale. Neither in Turkey nor in England were they ever to meet.

In September, 1856, Miss Dix set sail from Liverpool for her native land, where she was again to take up the fight for more and better care for the insane. This continued until April, 1861, when the outbreak of the Civil War made other work appear more urgent. On April 20, Dorothea wrote a friend: ". . . I think my duty lies near military hospitals for the present . . . I have reported myself and some nurses for free service at the War Department and to the Surgeon General."

First to volunteer and already well known for her philanthropic work, it was doubly natural that later, when hospital services were undergoing reorganization, Miss Dix should be appointed "Superintendent of Women Nurses for All Military Hospitals." It was natural but perhaps as hasty as most appointments made under the stress of an unplanned-for war. Miss Dix was then nearly sixty years old, had had many serious bouts with tuberculosis and malaria, and was now, without any previous hospital training or nursing experience, to take on the supervision of immense, yet to be organized departments at twenty different centers. She was by nature careful and conscientious, and the task she set herself proved all but impossible of achievement.

Comments written by those who knew Dorothea Dix during the Civil War seem to indicate that although she never spared herself, the task gradually became too much for her — must, it would seem, have proved too great for any one human being. In her distress she was heard to exclaim, "This is not the work I would have my life judged by!"

She had for years been at work perfecting organization and discipline in insane asylums, and she sought to bring the same perfection of organization and discipline into the hastily assembled military hospitals. She disagreed, often violently, with prominent medical officials and regimental surgeons, for she tried to stand over the sick and wounded soldiers — so her biographer writes — "as the avenging angel of their wrongs." She was absolutely tireless in ferreting out abuses and in enforcing their correction, setting standards that, to many, seemed impractically high. Somehow this all sounds very much like Florence Nightingale.

Dr. Caroline Burghardt, who served as a nurse during the Civil War, later described Dorothea Dix in words of warm admiration and affection — a shy, retiring, sensitive woman who yet never flinched in doing battle for justice and gave no thought to her own popularity with nurses and surgeons, who soon learned she would promptly appear if they did anything less than their whole duty.

Secretary of War Stanton, who had had personal experience of the fickleness of popular acclaim, never let himself be turned against Dorothea Dix. Had she permitted, he would have had her honored publicly at some great meeting. But, like her British counterpart, she refused anything of the sort. As soon as the war was over, she rededicated herself to the cause of the insane.

At the age of eighty, Dorothea Dix — an invalid physically but mentally no less alert than ever — found refuge in the first asylum she had helped to found, in Trenton, New Jersey.

Here she remained an honored guest for the last five years of her life.

Somehow it seems particularly fitting that she who, in providing homes for the friendless and helpless, had never had time to own a home of her own nor received the slightest remuneration for her labors, should at last rest in the arms of her "first-born child," as she always affectionately called the asylum in Trenton. Cared for tenderly, visited and written to by the many, many people who loved her, her last years may have been painful but they could not have been unhappy.

CHAPTER V

Clara Barton

Born a year later than Florence Nightingale and destined to live a year longer, the baby Clara Barton arrived on Christmas Day, 1821, at the home of Captain Stephen Barton in the little town of Oxford, Massachusetts. She was by ten years the youngest of five children, so that she had, in effect, six parents to bring her up.

Simple, thrifty, disciplined, the Bartons never denied the youngest member of the household a warm, affectionate understanding, never tried to dominate her — feeling it their duty, rather, to help her develop to the full whatever hidden talents she might possess. By those good sturdy folk, rages and hysterics would have been regarded as the sinful self-indulgences they undoubtedly were.

It was natural that Clara's older sisters should take her education in hand. These schoolteachers began on her at so early an age that she later claimed she could never recall when she learned to read. By the time she entered school, she scorned mere one-syllable words and proudly announced she could "spell in artichoke."

Clara's brothers did their part. Stephen, the older and more intellectual, taught her mathematics and, later, bookkeeping, so that she presently was able to keep books for his business. David, the dashing younger brother, was more interested in the purebred horses he raised.

At the age of five, little Clara had already learned from him to ride bareback with only halter and bit to guide the high-spirited horses. He expected her to keep her seat well, for he had high standards of excellence in all things. Though it may sometimes have been hard for the tiny child to hold on, the lessons she then learned were to stand her in good stead later when she would find herself mounted on some trooper's horse, fleeing for her life in the course of a war where doctor and nurse immunity were as yet unknown.

It was natural that Clara should love the wild, exciting rides across open fields and that between her and this fearless brother there grew up a very special bond of affection. So it was not at all strange that when David seriously hurt his back in a fall from the ridgepole of a barn to the hard ground underneath, it was not to his mother or older sisters he turned but to the little one, now eleven, whose spirit was so like his. For her part, she understood this and regarded it as her own special privilege to serve him and to nurse him.

For two long years, until he finally regained his health, Clara stayed so close by her brother that her family grew worried about her health. Apparently, though, Clara never gave a moment's thought to entering nursing as a career. Perhaps if at some time chance had brought Clara — as it did Dorothea Dix — face to face with the conditions where the sick and poor had to be cared for, she might have felt the call, as did Dorothea, to see to it that something was done. She too had an active social conscience, but no urgent call to exercise it.

When Clara reached the age of fifteen, there came to town and to stay in the Barton home, a certain Mr. Fowler, a "phrenologist" who was supposed to be able to study the bumps on a person's skull and to determine from such a study that person's hidden talents and personality traits. Nowadays Mr. Fowler — really a highly respectable person — would have bypassed the bumps and set himself up as a psychologist, for he seems to have had rare insight into human nature.

When Mrs. Barton asked her guest how she might best bring out her shy, retiring daughter who had spent too long in a sickroom and now did not seem able to face the world, Mr. Fowler solemnly examined the girl's head and stated that she would always be shy for herself but would be fearless for others. Her sensitive nature would develop to the full only as responsibility was thrust upon her.

For a girl in a family such as the Bartons, responsibility meant one thing above all others — teaching school. So, at the age of fifteen, Clara Barton, like Dorothea Dix before her, put up her hair and down her skirts — trying to look as old as her youth and small stature would permit. Some of her pupils were to be as old as herself and definitely taller. Yet, though in her own life she had never been unduly disciplined, she understood discipline instinctively and never in her own classes had difficulties with it.

Tomboy that she was, she could throw a ball as straight and as far as any of the big boys. She won their admiration and respect before they could even begin to think up plans to confound the new and very young teacher. She presently became famous for the good discipline of her classes — so that it was a custom to place her in any school where there had been problems. She always managed to straighten them out.

After a considerable period of this, Clara decided she needed more education and enrolled in the Institute at Clinton, New York, where she astonished the faculty by insisting on taking every subject offered. Then on to Bordentown, New Jersey, for a visit that developed into a long stay.

In those days, New Jersey had no public schools. Laws provided for their establishment but the town fathers had done nothing to implement them. Clara, noticing many young boys idling in the streets, asked them why they were not in school. Regretfully they explained there were no schools for such as they, who could pay no tuition.

Immediately and typically, Clara's New England conscience stirred her to action. She approached the town fathers and managed to persuade them to start a public school, assuring them that if they supplied an empty building, they need pay her no salary until such time as they were convinced that her scheme was a success.

It was an immediate success, and in the course of the next two years she built this school up from nothing to a large, well-attended, highly respected institution which attracted many of the pupils who had formerly attended private schools. In fact it was too successful, for the town fathers — forgetting they owed it all to Clara's efforts — decided the undertaking was too heavy for a mere woman and put a man over her.

Clara had no wish to be a subordinate where once she had

reigned supreme. She was a thorough individualist — a quality that so far had served her well but was eventually to prove a handicap. In any case, she was very tired indeed, having been a teacher for nearly twenty years. Her voice, always her weakest point, was failing her. At the age of thirty-five, she withdrew from the schoolroom, never, as it developed, to return.

She moved to Washington, where she promptly secured work as a clerk in the Patent Office. There it was her duty to copy in her fine, even handwriting the documents submitted in connection with applications for patents. In those pre-typewriter days, good copyists were much in demand. The first woman to be so employed in a government office, Clara did the work and received the pay of a man — $1400 a year.

Portraits of Clara Barton made at this time show a small, slight woman with brown hair drawn back from a smooth forehead. Her eyes seem dark and expressive, her nose straight, her mouth rather large and, even in repose, slightly turned up as in a half-smile. Perhaps she was not a beautiful woman but she must have been very attractive indeed. That several young men found her so there are numerous records to prove.

But Clara never married. At this time Clara could not have foreseen her life's dedication, could have had no such impulse as Florence Nightingale's to reject even the man she adored. Though it appears she did not adore any one man, she never expressed herself as averse to matrimony. Perhaps there were too many men clamoring for her affections. Perhaps there was no one particularly outstanding in the group.

That Clara liked at least three of the men well enough to give their claims serious consideration and felt unhappy to see each go out of her life, one may conclude both from her diary and from letters she wrote at the time. But as each grew impatient and demanded a final answer, she searched her heart, decided it was not deeply enough involved, and answered "No."

Nor was this the end to all men in her life. Much later — so a niece recorded — she went so far as to purchase a white satin gown and to make hints that some very special occasion was in the offing. Her relatives believed that there was a man, an important statesman whose name they knew but never revealed, to whom she expected to be married shortly. This man died and Clara never used her white satin gown.

Clara was still working in Washington when Fort Sumter was fired upon and when the first disastrous battle of Bull Run was fought. She went immediately to the hospitals to volunteer for help but found that there were more than enough women in Washington to take care of the wounded who were brought there at that time.

She remained, however, to talk to the wounded men and was shocked to hear their tales of cruel suffering on the field, of the comrades who had died there needlessly for want of prompt aid. She realized at once that the hospitals were too far away and that supplies and facilities for the care of the wounded must be brought to the very battlefields if thousands more were not to be carelessly sacrificed.

This Clara took to be her own problem. "Everybody's business," she once said, "is nobody's business. I intend to make nobody's business my business."

While others were just beginning to perceive some of the places of greatest need and were still talking about organizing some kind of relief, Clara wasted no time. She wrote at once to newspapers at home in Massachusetts and in New Jersey offering to distribute such materials as the women might wish to send for the care of the wounded. Sewing circles and ladies' aid societies organized and sent a flood of everything from bandages to delicacies for sick diets.

Clara began by sorting and repacking these articles for shipment to the regiments. But always in the back of her mind was the urgent thought that the men should not have to wait upon the conveniences of overcrowded and slow supply trains. Every hour that passed between the time a man was wounded and the time he received medical care and decent food might spell the difference between life and death. Those were days when lockjaw and blood poisoning were so common that a slightly wounded man, once infected, could well die, whereas a more severely wounded comrade, uninfected, would survive. Supplies and aid must go directly to the front. She would not gamble in sending them; she would take them herself. With her father, an old soldier, Clara discussed this plan, securing his approval.

Governor Andrews of Massachusetts had to be persuaded of the wisdom of Clara's plan and his approval secured. Troops, though fighting in a national cause, were still under the surveillance of their own states. Though the governor soon acquiesced, the Surgeon General, Dr. Hitchcock, did not, for he still belonged to that large group who shuddered at the thought of a woman at the front or even in a field hospital. Clara had to fight her way to the front.

Finally, in July, 1862, after many months' struggle with red tape, Clara received official permission from the Surgeon General: "Miss C. H. Barton has permission to go upon sick transports in any direction — for the purpose of distributing comforts to the sick and wounded — and nursing them . . ." With this permit, Clara's way was cleared. She did not, however, rush to the front but spent a few weeks touring New

England and New Jersey, explaining her plan, urging people
not to let the stream of supplies run thin. Then, her cart piled
high with these necessities, she set forth to Fredericksburg.

It must have been an odd sight that met the eyes of dignified
Washington churchgoers on that bright Sunday morning in
August — the mule cart lumbering down the streets with a
small, determined feminine figure perched on top. In the year
1862, Sundays were strictly kept and Clara knew she must
be shocking the sedate people, who looked upon her with startled eyes. So important, however, was her urgent mission that
she had no hesitation in starting out on Sunday. If she had not
been able to get off on Saturday, that, surely, was no reason to
keep the wounded waiting until Monday.

Clara's own words, written much later, best describe her
attitude and feelings on the occasion of her first going to the
front:

> When our armies fought on Cedar Mountain, I broke the
> shackles and went to the field. Five days and nights with
> three hours' sleep — a narrow escape from capture — and
> some days of getting the wounded into hospitals at Washing-
> ton brought Saturday, August 30. And if you chance to feel
> that the positions I occupied were rough and unseemly for a
> *woman* — I can only reply that they were rough and unseemly
> for *men*. But under all, lay the life of the Nation. I had
> inherited the rich blessing of health and strength of constitu-
> tion — such as are seldom given to woman — and I felt that
> some return was due from me and that I ought to be there.

On August 31, after the second battle of Bull Run, Clara
wrote a lengthy description of her experiences. She described
with a touch of humor her "coach" piled high with "boxes,
barrels, boards, and rails, which, in those days, seemed to help
me up and on in the world." She described the jostling trip
over rough country and the scene of her final destination:

". . . The ground, for acres, was a thinly wooded slope —
and among the trees, on the leaves and grass, were laid the
wounded . . . All day they came, and the whole hillside was
covered . . . three thousand suffering men crowded upon
the few acres within our reach." When she opened her stores,
she discovered that she had provided only "two water buckets,
five tin cups, one camp kettle, one stewpan, and a two-quart
tin dish, and three thousand guests to serve!"

The food was that which the womenfolk had placed in her
care and fortunately was in containers that might be turned
to use. Within fifteen minutes, wounds were being dressed
and food being cooked over open campfires which, no matter
which side she worked, always blew smoke into her face.

Imagine the scene if you can: Men laid close together on
thin beds of dry hay; surgeons and nurses moving about, their
way lit by lanterns and open candles. The slightest misstep
could have dropped a spark into the hay to envelop in flames
the whole mass of helpless men. So little space was left between these men that those trying to minister to them had,
now and again, to jolt one who was suffering painfully and
bring forth a torrent of groans. And through this scene moved
three women — Clara Barton and her two assistants, whom she
refers to only as "Mrs. Fales" and Mrs. M." Many of the men
to whom they brought supplies and succor would not otherwise have survived to reach the general hospitals in Washington.

By the middle of September, Clara had systematized her
method of operations. Haunted by the need for being first at
the front she would in the night bypass the resting military
supply trains. Never again was she to let herself be caught
without suitable equipment. Usually she was the only woman,
finding it better to take with her men strong enough to lift

burdens — such as helpless wounded men — too heavy for women.

Army officers were soon accustomed to the sight of this valiant little woman at the front. They gladly provided transportation when she needed it and offered her every courtesy. For her part, she found it a much less depressing experience to be working in the field within earshot and sometimes within actual range of enemy gunfire than among men brought to Washington hospitals and dying from infections that earlier care might have avoided.

Writing home after the battle of Antietam, September 16 and 17, she described her coming to a temporary hospital set up in the house and barn of a small farm. There, as usual, lay the wounded and dying and there labored the surgeons. Taking her arms full of stimulants and bandages, she followed the footpath to the house — to be met at the door by an astonished surgeon.

When, finally, he found his voice, he exclaimed, "God has indeed remembered us! How did you get from Virginia so soon? And again to supply our necessities . . . We have nothing but our instruments and the little chloroform we brought in our pockets. We have torn up the last sheets we could find in this house. We have not a bandage, rag, lint, or string, and all these shell-wounded men bleeding to death."

They set to work so close to the front that as Clara stooped to raise one man to give him a sip of water, a bullet sped between them, tearing a hole in her sleeve — killing the man. All day without letup they worked, and when darkness began to settle around them, Clara again won the doctor's undying regard by providing the lanterns that made it possible to continue into the night their work of mercy.

Clara had a way about her. The rough drivers who at first

rebelled against driving the loaded wagons into danger under a mere woman's direction became as gentle and as thoughtful of her as her own menfolk at home. There was something about her unhesitating plunge into work where the risk was greatest that set her apart from most other women.

The story goes that after the battle of Fredericksburg an officer, noticing her and thinking her to be one of the residents who had lost her home, asked gallantly, "Madam, you are alone and in danger. Do you want protection?"

Clara thanked him with a smile, adding that she believed herself to be the best protected woman in the whole United States.

The soldiers near by caught the words and cheered.

Even in the midst of a bitterly partisan war, Clara did not lose her sense of proportion or her deep sympathy with all human suffering. While she was working among the troops at Harpers Ferry, a large drove of cattle destined for army consumption came by. The officer in charge, a kind and conscientious man, came to her in distress. Over yonder, he explained, was a house used by Confederate surgeons, who were begging for meat lest their patients die of starvation.

"I am a bonded officer," the unhappy young man explained, "and responsible for property under my charge. What can I do?"

"Nothing, of course," replied Clara promptly, adding quietly, "but I am neither bonded nor responsible."

Taking the hint, the young man hurried off to the head of the drove while Clara arranged to have a large ox detached from the rear and driven into the fenced yard about the house.

"The last I saw of the white ox," she wrote with the kind of humor that must have endeared her to the men with whom she had to deal, "he had gone completely over to the enemy."

Battle by battle, Clara fought her way through the war, holding at bay the death that otherwise might have overtaken so many wounded men. For nearly three years she was an entirely independent worker with no organizational problems. Then, undoubtedly very tired and probably convinced the Sanitary Commission had well in hand the problem of bringing supplies and assistance to the front, she accepted an official appointment. From June 18, 1864, until the end of the war she remained at Point of Rocks, Virginia, as "Superintendent of the Department of Nurses of the Army of the James."

Not yet able to rest when the war ended, Clara dedicated her efforts to locating missing men — alive, if possible. In this she had a very personal interest, for her own brother Stephen, who before the war had taken residence in the the South, had long been missing only to turn up a broken and dying man. It took a woman's imagination to visualize the years of hoping and waiting involved in the little word "missing." The women thanked her for her interest from the bottom of their hearts. Not so all of the missing men. Some of them, it developed, emphatically wanted to remain missing.

Though such as these were quick to denounce Clara Barton as an interfering busybody, she soon felt there were far too few of them. Too many of the missing, she discovered, lay in unmarked graves at Andersonville. And because there seemed to be nobody else to undertake it, she assumed the task, gruesome though it must have been, of having those sad remains reinterred and seeing to it that the graves were decently marked. Though she was eventually reimbursed, partially, at least, by her government, she had to carry the expenses out of her own pocket from her savings from years of schoolteaching.

Small, essentially frail, exhausted by labors that well might have wrecked a more rugged constitution, Clara was still not ready to rest. Partly to recoup her finances, mostly because she wanted an opportunity of reporting directly to soldiers' families, she embarked upon a lecture tour on which she showed herself to be an exceptionally gifted platform speaker.

She traveled the length and breadth of the Northern states, telling of her experiences to large, enthusiastic, deeply moved audiences. But in 1868, flesh and blood reached the limits of its endurance and her voice gave out completely even as she stood on the platform facing a large expectant audience.

As usual in that era, a long trip abroad was prescribed. Clara's biographers, with the delicacy typical of close friends and relatives, do not make clear how she secured funds for this trip. Someone, one may guess, must, during the postwar boom, have shrewdly invested the money Clara had been earning and saving. In any case, she was able to take the trip in 1869, and always thereafter seemed to have an income sufficiently large to provide for her needs in real comfort though not conspicuous luxury.

Though Clara was supposed to be taking a complete rest, she could not close her eyes and ears to the world about her. It was only natural that while she was visiting Switzerland she should learn of the new Red Cross and that she should be asked why her own country held itself aloof from such an organization.

She who had worked so unceasingly in relief for the sick and wounded during her country's recent war must surely have felt the importance of an organization whose aim was to lessen needless suffering. She did feel it and lamely tried to explain the reluctance of her countrymen on the grounds that they really knew nothing about the Red Cross, the documents all being in foreign tongues.

Clara herself was soon to experience the power of the protection of this new organization. On July 15, 1870, the Franco-Prussian War broke out, and those who knew of Clara's work during the Civil War asked her to help direct relief work. Characteristically, Clara forgot that she was in Europe for a complete rest and threw herself into work for the wounded on battlefields, and behind the lines into civilian relief. Her own words best describe the impact of the Red Cross upon her:

> As I journeyed on and saw the work of these Red Cross societies in the field, accomplishing in four months under their systematic organization what we failed to accomplish in four years without it — no mistakes, no needless suffering, no starving, no lack of care, no waste, no confusion, but order, plenty, cleanliness, and comfort wherever that little flag made its way, a whole continent marshaled under the banner of the Red Cross — as I saw all this, and joined and worked in it, you will not wonder that I said to myself, "If I live to return to my country, I will try to make my people understand the Red Cross and that treaty."

This was a promise she made to others as well as herself. She was not a person to make a promise lightly or forget it easily. From the close of the war until the year 1881, through frustration and heartbreak, she labored to persuade her country to subscribe to the Treaty of Geneva. Then, having finally succeeded — through sheer persistence and a determined inability to acknowledge defeat — she was persuaded to accept the presidency of the American organization.

Clara Barton said that she felt the President of the United States should be titular head of the Red Cross, just as rulers in European countries were heading the societies in their own lands. But President Garfield persuaded her that no one but she could guide the destinies of the struggling infant organization.

This she did with characteristic vigor — through disasters, floods, and war — until she reached the age of eighty-two and the task had grown in dimensions beyond the power of any one woman, young or old to supervise. It would have been well for her if she had retired before. Having worked so hard to bring it into being, Clara had the mother's weakness of identifying herself with her child. She was the Red Cross and felt accountable to no one for her handling of society affairs. This, plus a complete inability to delegate authority, gradually made her position as head of a large national organization untenable.

So, in 1904, Clara Barton retired from her official position as president of the American Red Cross but emphatically did not retire from active life. At an age when most women — even those who had never had long bouts with illness — become old ladies and remain protected from the outside world, Clara was still making long journeys alone as need or interest might suggest, keeping up a voluminous correspondence, or simply running her home. She always rose early to feed the hens or weed the garden about her large, impressive home in Glen Echo, Maryland. She was a small, unpretentious, but not unimpressive woman whom many Americans liked to refer to as their Florence Nightingale.

Nothing, though, is so unfair as to label one person with another's name. Clara was not a Florence Nightingale, save in courage, breadth of vision, and personal dedication; she was emphatically herself with her own special and unique field of service.

America's grand old lady — as Jane Addams admiringly referred to her — she died in 1912. Above the resting place beside the graves of her forebears in the little cemetery in North Oxford, rises a monument topped with a red granite cross. Her greatest monument is no cross of stone but the living, enduring American Red Cross, which was created thanks to her vision and persistence and as the result of her own bitter personal experience of suffering and war.

Charles Sumner, famous statesman and orator, summed up her qualities — "the talent of a statesman, the command of a general, the heart and hand of a woman." What greater tribute could any woman desire?

CHAPTER VI

Mary Ann Bickerdyke

Also a dedicated woman, Many Ann Bickerdyke had the more personal dedication of a simpler, less highly educated, but no less single-minded soul. For her, the first consideration was always her "boys" — the ones who had volunteered and were brought suffering into her hospital or were negligently left upon the battlefield. Even as, in the chill night after a battle, she would walk the blood-soaked fields searching for any sign of breath in the white-faced bodies lying there — so, later in life, she would search civilian hospitals or even jails for ill or wayward "boys" whom she might reclaim to a better or more useful life. Hers was a devotion — biased and passionate —

that justly earned her the name by which she was affection·
ately known, Mother Bickerdyke.

Born Mary Ann Ball in Ohio on July 19, 1817, she came
from simple pioneer stock. Little is known for certain of her
early life or education. Even the most painstaking biographers
have failed to throw much light on her background. If she had
much formal education, she could not have set much store by
it, for she made a point of talking in blunt, ungrammatical, if
very effective phrases.

By the time the Civil War broke out, Mary Ann had been
married and widowed with two children of her own and several
stepchildren to support. She was a resident of Galesburg, Illinois, and a member of Dr. Edward Beecher's congregation.
Son of the famous Lyman Beecher and brother of both Henry
Ward Beecher and Harriet Beecher Stowe (famous author
of *Uncle Tom's Cabin*), Edward Beecher must surely have
been a movingly eloquent speaker for the cause of the Union.
It was thanks to his influence upon the members of his congregation that Mary Ann was sent, laden with supplies, to
the post hospital at Cairo, Illinois, to visit the Galesburg boys
there and to make certain their interests were being properly
looked after.

Just why Mrs. Bickerdyke was selected for this task is not
too clear. One person who wrote of her during her lifetime
mentions her "well-known skill as a nurse"— which may mean
that in Galesburg she supported her fatherless family by helping out in homes where there was illness. It certainly does not
suggest any experience in institutional nursing, for, remember,
there was at that time almost none at all anywhere in America.
Perhaps it was that Mary Ann's emotions responded more
quickly to Dr. Beecher's plea and that she, in her typically
blunt speech, expressed her feelings promptly.

In any case, Mary Ann went to Cairo in June, 1861, and from then on, until after the end of the war, served in army hospitals. Though she was old enough and, from all accounts, plain enough to meet Miss Dix's published standards, apparently Mrs. Bickerdyke never held an official appointment from the superintendent of nurses. It seems that her untiring competence was soon recognized by army officers in charge of areas where she appeared and that they asked her to assist in the care of the sick and wounded. Presently — in recognition of her selfless devotion and in order to give a measure of legitimacy to her position — she was given some kind of appointment as an agent for the Northwestern Sanitary Commission. Official appointments and official regulations never interested her.

After the battle of Donelson, a surgeon came upon her before a campfire, cooking food for the shivering, fainting, wounded men. He watched with admiration as she dispensed the much-needed nourishment and skillfully applied temporary dressings to wounds.

"Madam," he finally remarked, "you seem to combine in yourself a sick-diet kitchen and medical staff. May I inquire under whose authority you are working?"

She was not, of course, under anyone's authority and answered promptly, "I have received my authority from the Lord God Almighty; have you anything that ranks higher than that?"

Apparently even General William Tecumseh Sherman was under the same impression. Once when Mother Bickerdyke found a surgeon negligent in the care of her boys and peremptorily ordered him to remove his shoulder straps, he appealed to the general.

"Who was your accuser?" asked General Sherman. "Who made the charges?"

When told it was "that spiteful old woman, Mrs. Bickerdyke," Sherman shrugged his shoulders and replied, "Oh, well, then if it was she, I can't help you. She has more power than I — she ranks me."

To feed and care for her boys, Mary Ann Bickerdyke would stop at nothing. When government supplies ran short, she set out on foraging expeditions. Though she would not, undoubtedly, have been averse to liberating Confederate hens or pigs, she paid for what she could buy when she had the money. When she had not, she used for barter the clothes friends sent her to replace those of her own that had been damagd by sparks from the campfires. Her boys, she once explained, were always finding it necessary to "put me out."

When money and other resources came to an end, Mary Ann ran up bills and sent them on to the Chicago Sanitary Commission, blandly expecting that any accounts run up in behalf of her boys would be covered gladly by folks in the safety of civilian homes. Covered they were, but not always as easily as she assumed, for funds had to come from somewhere and records had to be kept and accountings made. However, though they vainly tried to impress on her some system of requisitioning, the officials of the Sanitary Commission always recognized her integrity and devotion by honoring her bills, even if the means for so doing occasionally came out of their own pockets.

When she found that it was becoming increasingly difficult to purchase good fresh milk and eggs for her boys — the quality growing daily more doubtful — Mother Bickerdyke took a trip to the North to round up a hundred cows and a thousand hens. She returned to Memphis in triumph "amid immense lowing and crowing and cackling," informing astonished citizens, "These are *loyal* cows and hens; none of your miserable trash that give chalk and water for milk, and lay foul-smelling eggs."

General Hurlbut, at that time in charge in Memphis, assigned her an island in the river and there her cows and hens remained loyally supplying all the city's hospitals — at least as long as Mother Bickerdyke remained in the city.

Soon after her arrival in Cairo, Mary Ann had taken charge of the hospital there and now in Memphis was in charge of the Gayoso Hospital, which once had been the best hotel in the city. Vigorous in her administration, she had the hospitals cleaned and scrubbed until they shone, planned and supervised the feeding of the sick men, salvaged the filthy clothing in which they had been brought in, having it washed and mended for future issue. Her hospitals set standards the whole Medical Department should have aimed at — the food excellent, the nursing exceptionally skilled, the administration economical and efficient.

When the Northwestern Sanitary Commission outfitted boats to transport the sick men up the Mississippi River to places of greater safety and less crowding, Mrs. Bickerdyke took upon herself the task of supervising and equipping the boats, nursing the men during their trips north. After the fall of Vicksburg, she moved her headquarters there — then away from the river and on to Jackson, Mississippi. She followed General Sherman's troops in their march to Atlanta and would not have hesitated to accompany them to the sea if he had not commanded her to withdraw. Tactfully, he suggested that she collect food and supplies with which to meet him and his troops at Savannah.

But when General Sherman's troops arrived at Savannah, they looked — to the maternal eyes of Mary Ann Bickerdyke

— disgustingly healthy and well fed. So, on her own initiative, she diverted her shipful of supplies to the aid of the pitiful Andersonville victims, now beginning to drag themselves north.

She was soon back in a hospital and at her usual work. This time it was in Beaufort, North Carolina, where Mary von Olnhausen recorded her impressions in a letter written home on April 30, 1865:

> . . . Did I tell you about Mrs. Bickerdyke, who has come down here from the Western army and is cooking for this hospital? She is perfectly splendid. To be sure, she snubs me and everybody else; but, Lord, how she works, and what good things she makes; our men are better fed than they would be at home, even the best of them. . . . she talks bad grammar and jaws us all, but I don't care; her heart is the best, and she will make every soldier live . . . She is never afraid of any one. Dr. S., of Alexandria, was around inspecting her kitchen, drunk. He found fault with everything; she took him by the nape of the neck, led him out, called a guard, and told them to take this drunken man to headquarters and she would have him court-martialled. He was afterwards glad enough to apologize and get out of that place, or she would have done it, sure.

Certainly the most vigorous, the most outspoken, the least polished of the three women here sketched, Mrs. Bickerdyke must also have been the most essentially feminine. She had a woman's intense and partisan devotion, fighting for those under her care with a fierce violence that overcame all obstacles. Though her hospitals were models of organization for her era, she had the instincts of a bedside nurse, not of a nurse-executive. It did not occur to her any more than to the large majority of Civil War nurses to carry her experience into wider fields —

to dedicate it to the improvement of all hospitals and nursing services in her own time and for years to come.

Mother Bickerdyke's interest was her children — her "boys." For them she would make any sacrifice, challenge any superior officer. A lioness with her cubs could be no more fearsome. But when her boys had been cared for, she was content to let the rest of the world care for itself.

As long as she lived, Mother Bickerdyke continued to espouse the cause of her boys. After she died, her boys still kept her memory green, remembering with affection the tender devotion she held for them. But when the last of her boys died the cause for which she had lived also died and Mother Bickerdyke was finally laid to rest.

In our day, even the most partisan of biographers can hardly bring Mary Ann Bickerdyke to life. Such is the inevitable fate of mothers — such has been the fate of most of the hundreds of women who left their homes and families to serve in army hospitals, often at the risk of their own health and always without personal profit. Their country will always owe them an incalculable debt. The nursing profession owes them, unfortunately, no more than an increased acceptance of the idea that hospital nursing was a fit and acceptable occupation for a lady.

CHAPTER VII

Kate Cumming

To the south of the invisible Mason-Dixon Line which divided this nation into two violently warring parts were other women, quite as convinced as their Northern sisters of the justice of the cause for which their menfolk were fighting and dying. Fundamentally this cause was a belief in their own way of life — in great estates almost feudal in their extent and management, with a small, highly educated white gentry and a great body of black serfs. Here there was an extremely limited industrial development and practically no middle class.

The educated women of the Confederacy belonged to a narrow group in many ways more exclusive than the British aristocracy and quite as devoted to the aristocratic tradition. It was natural for these women — as it had been for noble ladies since the days of chivalry — to wish to tend the men who were fighting and dying for them. Had they not, in addition, the very recent example of the exploits of a highly placed British lady whose praises were still ringing in their ears?

But the men were fighting not only for their women but for their way of life. To permit these women to enter military hospitals as nurses was somehow to accept defeat from within. Even in their hours of extremest need, Southern gentlemen found it hard to consent to having their plantation-bred, carefully protected women take upon their delicate shoulders the truly revolting tasks of serving wounded and dying men — men who were mostly strangers to them and often to their way of life.

To select wounded heroes and bring them into their homes for care was not, of course, unfit for ladies in such times of stress, even if the heroes proved to be poor whites and not quite acceptable socially. To this extent wounds were great levelers, and so far might the ladies be permitted to strain their nobility. But no farther, insisted most of the men.

The ladies, however, proved to have minds of their own. The limited help which they could give in their own homes only helped to impress upon them the greater need which they were not permitted to fill. How could they talk with men who had been through the hell of war or tend the tortured few they encountered without perceiving this? And then the calls began to come.

Kate Cumming, Scottish by inheritance, Confederate by residence and sympathy, wrote of her war experiences in her *Journal of Hospital Life,* published in Louisville, Kentucky, in 1866. Later, in 1892, when the bitterness of war had somewhat abated, she wrote a longer and more detailed account under the title *Gleanings from the Southland.* This, as she explains, was published in the hope of giving Northerners some idea of the South and its problems.

From these two journals, the writer emerges as a figure of unusual intelligence, courage, and insight who, had she resided to the north of the Line, would have been in the field, tending the men as they fell. But even the spirited Miss Cumming could not achieve this in her South. Her determination to go into a hospital was in itself sufficiently radical, for she admits, "I must confess, from all I had heard or seen, for a while I wavered about the propriety of it; but when I remembered the suffering I had witnessed and the relief I had given, my mind was made up to go into one if allowed to do so . . ."

Her own call came while she was visiting in Mobile. Like that in Galesburg, Illinois — and so many others both North and South — it was issued in a church. The Southern minister seems to have been more realistic than his more practical neighbors, for he did not hesitate to plead eloquently with the ladies to go into hospitals as nurses. Like Kate Cumming, most of the ladies present had never been inside any hospital and had not the vaguest idea as to what one might be like or what kind of services might be expected of them there. Yet they responded promptly, even eagerly, certain they had power to meet any demands. As the spirited Kate, mindful of Florence Nightingale, remarked, "I knew what one woman had done, another could."

Then came the task of convincing their menfolk. Surprisingly, it was not with the older, usually more conservative, generation that Kate had her troubles. Her father, possibly fully as Scottish as Confederate, readily gave his consent to this step. The violently opposing voices came from the younger men of the family, and brothers-in-law at that.

One of these loudly insisted that "no sister of his should take

such a step," while another proclaimed with equal conviction
that a lady could not nurse soldiers and remain "refined" — in
other words, remain a lady. The third, who perceived Kate
might have dreams of becoming another Florence Nightingale,
sought to deflate her by reminding her that his mother and
sister had nursed with Miss Nightingale in the Crimea, so that
he knew all about such things. This, he insisted, was to be a
totally different war. Her position could not be at all like
theirs, "for they went under the auspices of a powerful government who gave them every assistance, while ours was too
poor to give us any."

How sadly Florence Nightingale might have smiled had she
heard these words and reflected that less than ten years had
dimmed the memory of her very bitter struggles in the Crimea
so far away from the powerful government under whose auspices she went out and whose "every assistance" had so often
proved too little too late. History had perhaps not yet made
this clear, for Kate Cumming apparently did not have any answer ready for the argument save that she was determined to go
wherever she was needed, whatever the consequences to her
status as a lady.

"My subsequent experience," she later wrote, "proved that
none, excepting the most high-toned and refined women, had
any business doing that most sacred of all duties — alleviating
suffering . . ."

Yet even after the decisions were made and acted upon, pressure from the menfolk continued. Friends frequently advised
the women to go home from the hospital, "as it was not respectable to go into one." A fellow nurse received a letter from a
cousin who was a surgeon in the Confederate army, begging
her to leave the hospital because it was "no place for a refined,
modest young lady." And all about were the sly, derogatory

remarks that must have undermined many a nurse's determination. Miss Cumming sums it up in the words, "I think that if any credit is due them at all, it is for the moral courage they have in braving public opinion."

It did, of course, take far more than this. For here, as in the Union hospitals, a very special kind of courage was needed. Conditions were such that many nurses of today would have difficulty facing them without flinching. As in the North, men were brought in from the battlefields in filthy blankets and laid upon floors to await the all too limited care available. The floor, which there was always too little time to mop, was frequently awash with bloody water spilled while the men were being bathed. The air was so foul as to be almost unbreathable and, worst of all, as Miss Cumming wrote, "The amputating room is in our passage to the kitchen and many a time I have seen the blood flow in streams from under the door. I often wish I could become as callous as many appear for there seems to be no end to the horrors."

Here also, infectious diseases took their toll, so that she was moved to exclaim that the enemy must be in no better state or "they could annihilate us with ease." With surprising lack of partisan bitterness, she went on to comment, "These were the stern realities that were transpiring daily and hourly in every hospital, North and South."

No wonder, then, that even in this stronghold of the aristocratic tradition, taboos finally gave way. One tourist from England, who must have had to listen to many arguments on both sides of the question, finally wrote home that "some women went into hospitals because it was too terrible to stay away . . . and because they could not do otherwise."

For army-hospital nursing, North or South, the Civil War marked the end of an era. Whatever arguments against nursing the menfolk of the future might think up, rarely again would they claim that modest and refined young women could not nurse in hospitals and remain ladies. Never again would be taken for granted the hastily assembled, ill-equipped hospitals, staffed by untrained women appearing from nowhere, their arms filled with all too needed supplies; women who, when urged, might stay to comfort and feed the sick, to assist, untrained as they were, the overworked surgeons, and, finally, to defy authority which seemed to them — and often may well have been — quite arbitrary. Such individualists, splendid though they may have been in the stress of that war, wanted no place in nursing as a disciplined profession. For old days and ways were passing and progress was making its new and urgent demands.

CHAPTER VIII

Linda Richards, America's First
Trained Nurse

Too few of the world's great nurses have — as far as the general reading public is concerned — become articulate about their lives and their profession. Too few have been able to take time out from their busy lives to leave a record for the enlightenment of those who are to come after. Yet if we are to appreciate these women and to understand the progress of their profession, we should know the backgrounds from which they came and the impulses behind their choice of their life's work.

Certainly it must have been more than mere chance or excitement over the exploits of a legendary figure during the

Crimean War that brought into being the formal training of nurses in America and made American women both proud and eager to enter it. Out of our own Civil War grew the increased awareness of nursing. Even the most inarticulate of the hundreds of women who had served in army hospitals must have come home with thrilling, if hair-raising, tales of nursing there. Their patients, invalided home, could not have been altogether silent.

The sum of all these influences must have decided many young women to undertake a career of nursing. In one of those rare documents left behind by nurses, Linda Richards explains her own impulse: "My desire to become a nurse grew out of what I heard of the need of nurses in the Civil War. Long before the organization of training schools in America, I had a fixed purpose to devote my life to the work of caring for the sick and suffering . . ." Born in 1841 and growing up in her grandfather's home in a small town in western New York State, she presently demonstrated that indefinable set of qualities that made the neighbors call her a "born nurse."

A born nurse could expect to be called on day or night, as illness in the neighborhood might require, and would be proud to answer the call, never expecting the slightest remuneration. Such a person had, it seemed, in addition to her special nursing abilities, a social obligation to answer the call of duty wherever and whenever it might sound. Young Linda definitely enjoyed this work, though later she was to wonder how her crude nursing had found such favor in the eyes of her patients and their friends.

Fully determined to become a nurse, she realized that she needed special training in the art of nursing. In those days, of course, opportunities for such training were not easily to be found, so that Linda felt especially fortunate when she had a chance to enter the Boston City Hospital as an assistant in a large ward.

Though a kind woman and sympathetic with Linda's ambitions, the head nurse was untrained and completely unequipped to give instruction, as the young assistant soon recognized. She administered medicines of which she knew neither the name nor the action. She had no understanding of symptoms, and only an uncommon good sense made her aware of signs of danger. Even so, she was unquestionably superior to many who nursed in the hospital, for she had a genuine desire to serve humanity, whereas others who worked there might be thoughtless, careless, or even heartless.

Even the novice could see that the wards were badly kept. The nurses' quarters were bad, their food was poor, and they themselves were treated without respect by everyone in the hospital. Small wonder, then, that Linda Richards soon decided that in this environment she could never become the kind of nurse she wished to be.

Fortunately, at this critical time she learned that training was to be made available at the New England Hospital for Women and Children. It sounded like the kind of training she had been dreaming of, so she immediately offered herself to Dr. Dimock (her junior by six years) and became in 1872 the first enrollee of the new school.

The work was hard but Linda was well satisfied with it, for she was at last making progress toward her life's goal. No eight-hour days for her! Rising at 5:30 A.M. she worked in the wards until, at 9 P.M., she retired to a little room between the wards. But not to sleep — for each nurse took care of her six patients both day and night, so that she often had to answer as many as nine calls during a night and found sleep all but impossible. There were no uniforms — the only stipulation being that dresses worn by the nurses should be washable.

Presently, after six months of such a regime, special nurses were assigned to night work so that the day nurses might rest. The nurses were given no time to themselves save one afternoon every second week. Women interns were in charge of instructing the nurses in practical procedures, and under this tutelage they learned such tasks — previously regarded as outside mere woman's grasp — as taking pulse, respiration, and even temperatures. Special care was observed that the nurses should not know the names of the medicines they administered.

It is only fair to point out here that this insistence on secrecy may have been due not so much to a lack of belief in the nurses' intelligence as to a belief in their too great intelligence — a secret fear that they might learn too much about medicine and thus be able to compete with the doctors. In the intervening years it has grown less and less fashionable to administer medicines in the quantities and varieties then administered by physicians and expected by their patients. Nowadays even the most ignorant layman can purchase almost anything save a few forbidden dangerous drugs at the corner drugstore. But then doctors knew much less of the causes of disease than they have since learned and, consequently, based their treatments on medicines which might allay symptoms, real or imaginary, and thus win the confidence of their patients. Secret formulas — Dr. Thingamabobby's Elixir for this or that — were all too common, and even those physicians who would not stoop to commercializing their formulas could still guard them jealously.

To do further justice to the medical profession of that time, one should realize that clinical thermometers were a relatively newfangled invention. No one can appreciate the value of this present-day household commonplace who has not had the privilege of hearing a real old-time doctor reminisce and tell how marvelous he found that simple device when, about the year 1870, it first became generally available. With it he could determine, by a method more accurate than that of placing his hand on the flushed brow, whether his patient was running a temperature and just how much he was running. Naturally, the first clinical thermometers must have been quite costly, and the physician would therefore be reluctant to entrust such a delicate instrument to the hands of inexperienced young women. It took the women doctors to appreciate that sex should be no handicap and that nurses who could take temperatures would be more useful than nurses who could not.

In any case, the training received by Linda Richards in 1872 and 1873 was all too limited, so that later she was to marvel how she and her classmates turned out to be of any use at all. "It does not seem quite loyal to my school," she wrote, "to tell how very little training we received, for everyone in authority gave us of her best nursing knowledge."

Apparently, even with this limited knowledge, Miss Richards was regarded as highly employable, for on graduation she received several flattering offers. After much weighing of pros and cons, she decided to take a position as night superintendent in the Bellevue Hospital training school that had recently been organized in New York.

Patterned on the Nightingale school in London, Bellevue had an English superintendent, Sister Helen of All Saints' Order. A strong and often forbidding disciplinarian, Sister Helen had recently taken in hand the badly run hospital and was in the process of bringing order there.

Linda Richards found many things in Bellevue entirely beyond the scope of her previous experience. The patients came from slums such as she had never dreamed of, and she had to learn to see beneath their often uninviting exteriors to human beings fundamentally no different from others she had known. The wards, she found, were large, dismal places made more dismal at night when heat and illuminating gas were turned off and she had to move about in clammy cold by flickering candlelight.

The first reform she was to bring about was to remedy this. Her pleas finally persuaded the warden not to turn off all gas at night, under her solemn — and conscientiously kept — promise never to burn more gas than was absolutely essential to the fulfillment of her duties. She was also to inaugurate there the modern method of keeping case records, the first ones she kept for her own reference having proved so useful to the doctors in charge that they soon requested written records of all cases.

Perhaps the most needed reform of all was the isolation of maternity cases. Childbed fever in the hospital had reached epidemic proportions and women were dying daily. The large, unsanitary ward for waiting women was made more gloomy by the fact that the patients had to sit there and sew shrouds. "I used to wonder," wrote Linda Richards, "if they speculated as to whether they were making their own." Cheerful place!

Complete removal of all such cases from the hospital building was finally arranged, the women being sent to a pavilion on Blackwell's Island where, finally, the dread fever was stamped out. Though Miss Richards made no personal claim for the reform, she may have been at least partly responsible for it. In Boston, the great Dr. Oliver Wendell Holmes had, as early as 1843, been the first to point out that childbed fever might be avoided by careful attention to cleanliness and by isolation of the mother from other patients. Miss Richards had just come from a Boston hospital where the influence of his teachings must surely have been felt.

Another reform which took place during Linda Richards's stay at Bellevue — a reform which she does not mention in her memoirs and with which, therefore, she may have had little to do — was the adoption of a uniform by the student nurses. Apparently such a step had been under consideration for some time by those in charge, but the students had rebelled at the merest suggestion of anything that might be regarded as a livery — a servant's uniform. This, they feared, was just another attempt to show the nurse her place and to keep her in a position of inferiority and subjection.

Fortunately for progress, though, there was in that first class at Bellevue a young lady of the aristocratic family and name of Van Rensselaer. If Miss Van Rensselaer could be persuaded to put herself into uniform, no one would again talk of livery. Tall, elegant, aristocratic — she had no need of being afraid that anyone would mistake her for or treat her like a servant.

The young lady obligingly took a two days' vacation, to return to duty in a blue and white striped seersucker dress with starched white collar, cuffs, and apron. On her lovely head was a starched white cap. The costume was admittedly charming and soon all students were actually clamoring for ones of their own — so much more cheerful and practical than the clothes they had been wearing. It was not long before similar costumes were worn in all schools of nursing — the distinctive small details of color, cut, and material setting each school apart from the others.

In November, 1874, Linda Richards left Bellevue to return to Boston. This time it was to the Massachusetts General Hospital to a training school organized in 1873, for work in the hospital by an outside organization. Mary von Olnhausen, who had nursed in army hospitals during the Civil War, had been the first superintendent but she soon found that neither by training nor by temperament was she fitted for such work.

Linda Richards's first task as superintendent was to bring the school into closer association with the hospital, a project to which many doctors and surgeons were still violently opposed. Fortunately, however, there were on the board of the training school many influential Boston ladies, sisters of or otherwise closely related to the trustees of the hospital.

Unable, even in their moments of relaxation, to escape these insistent women, the trustees finally had to give in and adopt the school, assigning as a nurses' residence a recently remodeled building on the hospital grounds. The doctors were soon beginning to wonder how the hospital had ever been run without such a school and were graciously giving lectures to the students and taking them on rounds in the wards.

The annual report of the trustees of the hospital for the year 1883 remarks upon the progress made in the training school which had begun in 1873 with only six students experimentally assigned to two wards. By 1877 the nursing of the whole hospital had been assigned to the training school. At the time of the report it boasted, in addition to the superintendent of the whole school, a night superintendent, twelve head nurses, and forty-two pupils. With this rapid growth came rapid multiplication of duties, so that the superintendent became increasingly aware of the limitations of her own training and experience.

Linda Richards was possessed by the desire to go to England — "to spend some months in hospitals, to learn from them methods of training school work." The training-school committee of the Massachusetts General Hospital "entered into a correspondence in my behalf" with the ever influential Mr.

Rathbone, chairman of the St. Thomas's Hospital training-school committee, with the result that, in 1877, she received an invitation to go to England for a six months' visit.

With the delight of a pilgrim starting for the Promised Land, Linda Richards set sail. Though she expected no personal rewards beyond permission to work in St. Thomas's Hospital and to study the methods of nursing and training in use in that famous place, she was to see Miss Nightingale and have her life's dream realized. Still, she did not lose her head, and promptly set to work, though she confessed,

> Many things were strange to me at first. Mrs. Wardproper was always called "Matron" by every one in the hospital, never being addressed by her name. The head nurses were called Ward Sisters and were known by the names of the wards of which they had charge, as Sister Albert, Sister Victoria, Sister Ophthalmia [eye inflammation] and so on . . .

In the grate of the cheerful dining room of the nurses' home, a fire always burned and before it on the fender boiled a large teakettle from which each nurse might fill her own small teapot in order to serve herself, fresh and hot, the national drink. There were other customs even more strange to the visitor from America, but she soon was made to feel at home, finally even becoming accustomed to the glass of beer issued each nurse at lunch, dinner, and supper.

> The happy, instructive months at St. Thomas's passed quickly. Some two or three years after my visit there, a friend who was visiting the hospital wrote me that Mrs. Wardproper had spoken most kindly of me, saying that she thought me a very good woman to have gone over as the first American nurse, that I made no trouble, and seemed to appreciate the advantages given me.

What had Mrs. Wardproper expected in an American nurse? A feathered Indian, perhaps? One can only be grateful that Linda Richards, all unknowing, was able to quiet her fears.

Mrs. Wardproper must have changed her mind almost on the first meeting, because within four days Linda was invited to visit Florence Nightingale; this could hardly have occurred without consultation between Miss Nightingale and Mrs. Wardproper, who were acknowledged friends. Or could Florence herself have had some curiosity about this American?

In any case, to Linda Richards this visit was like a pilgrimage to a shrine. Florence Nightingale treated it as a business consultation. She graciously discussed the American visitor's plans and suggested that she enlarge her experience by visiting King's College Hospital in London as well as St. Thomas's and that later she go on to the Royal Infirmary of Edinburgh. Miss Nightingale's merest suggestion was, of course, gospel and her sponsorship of sufficient weight to open for the visitor even the tightest shut doors.

Linda Richards worked at King's College Infirmary a full month while she observed with interest the extremely strict rules of the St. John's Sisterhood (Episcopal), which was responsible for the nursing there. Her description of the work assigned to the night nurses will show something of those rules:

> Every nurse seemed to know and do her own duty, and that with few words. . . . In a double ward of twenty-four beds there were two night nurses; each nurse had her midnight meal on her own side of the ward, nor did they ever visit each other. Each ward had two very elaborate fireplaces, which were kept clean by the night nurses, who also had charge of the medicine closets, the pantries, and the bathrooms . . . A second custom even more odd was that of boiling potatoes before the ward fire so that they might be

served hot. The youngest probationer had this duty in charge.
All this made more work for the night nurse of twelve beds
than for our American night nurses of twenty beds . . .

Despite this additional work, Miss Richards remarks, there
seemed to be little complaint or rebellion against the strict
rules. Everyone seemed cheerful and helpful.

Presently she moved on to Edinburgh where she arrived on
a typical August morning, in 1877, when the beautiful and
historic old Scottish city was obscured by an almost equally
old Scottish mist. The Royal Infirmary turned out to be a
group of ancient gray stone buildings in an enclosure off the
cobblestoned streets of the old city. The situation had little to
justify it save age and tradition and its closeness to the medical
schools. But the infirmary was, like the other hospitals Miss
Richards had viewed in Great Britain, clean and comfortable
with a generally cheerful, hopeful atmosphere.

It was in the operating room here that the newcomer first
encountered the new and revolutionary antiseptic surgery and
the even newer and more radical aseptic surgery — such a
commonplace today that one can hardly realize that it was
barely known a mere seventy-five years ago. To her, as it had
so recently been to doctors and men of science, it must have
been an almost unbelievable revelation.

Children of an atomic age, who have no hesitation in accepting on faith the existence of things unseen and never to be
seen, must try to imagine the scientific world of a mere hundred years ago, when the atomic theory was still a theory and
no one had dreamed up electrons — when bacteria had been
seen under the then crude microscopes but no one had as yet
demonstrated their relationship to disease. To understand the
conditions in hospitals of the 1860's and the changes brought
about by the end of the 1870's, one must understand some of

the work done outside the walls of those hospitals in the labo-
ratories of "impractical" men of science.

It was about the year 1670, in the city of Leyden, Holland,
that a nearsighted lens grinder named Leeuwenhoek looked
through some of his new lenses and saw tiny organisms, otherwise invisible, which grew and multiplied before his watching eyes. How much longer would the world have had to wait
for this epoch-making discovery, if the lenses of the lens grinder's own eyes had not already had the excessive magnification
of all nearsighted eyes? With this magnification to add to that
of the new lenses he had made, there was first revealed to his
startled vision the existence of microorganisms such as bacteria. On such slim-chance combinations is scientific progress
frequently built.

Yet the world had to wait nearly one hundred and seventy-
five years — until the 1840's — for the first experiment pointing out a possible relationship between any microorganism
and the disease it caused. Still another twenty years passed before the French experimenter Davaine saw anthrax bacilli in
the blood of sick animals, transferred such blood to healthy
animals and watched these sicken and die while those to whom
he had transferred bacillus-free blood remained unaffected.

Meanwhile Louis Pasteur, working primarily on the spoilage
of wine and beer, was developing the means of growing microorganisms in flasks. Once this technique was established,
the race to discover and name organisms was on. Both Pasteur
in France and Robert Koch in Germany were shortly cultivat-
ing pathogenic organisms, studying them, and proving their
pathogenicity. In the years between 1870 and 1890, nearly
all those causing severe infections were isolated, studied, and
their damaging effects proved.

Small wonder, then, considering the ignorance of the times,

that during the wars of the 1850's and 1860's there were so many deaths from blood poisoning, lockjaw (tetanus), and gangrene. It is a wonder only that anyone anywhere had insight enough to urge isolation and cleanliness as a possible means of checking the terrible inroads of such infections. All surgery was done, all amputations were made with a grave appreciation of the risks involved but absolutely no understanding of why they existed or how they might be avoided.

By the late 1870's, the medical world was beginning to appreciate the significance of the work of the scientists, and one Joseph Lister (presently to be knighted for his lifesaving techniques), operating in the Edinburgh Infirmary, was beginning to do something about it. If microorganisms caused the terrible infections following surgery, then such aftereffects might be avoided by keeping the organisms away from the wounds or killing them after they got in.

Sir Joseph's radical idea was to operate while keeping hands, instruments, and wounds in a spray of antiseptic solution, usually carbolic acid. Not much later, the idea of aseptic surgery was to come in — the idea that infecting organisms could be kept away entirely and therefore would not have to be killed. It would still be some years — 1890, in fact — before rubber operating gloves would first be manufactured in America. Thus, between the middle 1840's, when general anesthesia was first introduced into an American operating room, and 1890, modern surgical procedure had been born.

Linda Richards was fortunate enough to make her start during these exciting years, and to come into immediate personal contact with the Lister method. She wrote of her Edinburgh experiences:

> In the well-equipped Fever House, separated as far as possible from the other buildings, I saw my first case of typhus

fever. For the first time I saw here tiled wards. Every possible precaution was used to prevent the spread of the disease. As is well known, it was in the Royal Infirmary that Professor Lister inaugurated his wonderful method of treating wounds, a stepping stone to the greatly improved methods with which all nurses of today are so familiar. At the time of my visit, Professor Lister had just gone to introduce his methods at King's College Hospital, while in the Royal Infirmary, Dr. Joseph Bell was carrying on advanced aseptic treatment of wounds. Professor Bell's Sunday Morning clinics given to the nurses exclusively, were a wonderful privilege . . .

Incidentally, Dr. Bell's was the tall, rugged figure and brilliantly inquiring mind that inspired one of his medical students, a certain Arthur Conan Doyle, to create the world-famous detective, Sherlock Holmes.

On her way back to London from her Edinburgh studies, Miss Richards stopped off at a little way station near Lea Hurst. There Miss Nightingale's coachman met her and brought her for a few days' visit with his famous mistress. One may be sure Linda Richards was delighted — also that the chief topic of conversation there was nursing and a comparison of English and American hospitals and methods. Later Florence wrote to Matron Pringle of the Royal Infirmary of this visit: ". . . I have seldom seen anyone who struck me as so admirable. I think we have as much to learn from her as she from us." To Linda Richards, taking ship for home about a month later after visiting hospitals in Paris, she wrote cordially, "May you outstrip us, that we in turn may outstrip you."

Miss Richards was, in very truth, returning to wider fields of endeavor. Before leaving for England, she had received hints that she was to be invited to organize a training school in connection with the Boston City Hospital. The nursing service at

that hospital had in no way improved since the days she had
first tried her hand at caring for the sick there and had left in
disgust because she was learning nothing.

Dr. Cowles, now medical superintendent, wanted a good
school of nursing, and for this purpose sought out the best,
most experienced, and most highly trained nurse he knew —
Linda Richards. She accepted the assignment, though not without fear and trembling — realizing as no one could nowadays
how much depended upon the success of her venture. If she
failed to train competent nurses and failed to convince the resident medical staff of their importance and usefulness, it could
be more than a personal failure. It might give the new, young
cause of nursing and of hospital training schools a serious set-
back.

Miss Richards did not fail. She not only established the
school, she soon saw to it that the program of training was ex-
panded to two years. She also managed to have the young
women relieved of some of the hardest, least productive work
— employing ward maids for much of the ward work. Thus
student nurses could perfect themselves in some of the more
professional tasks such as taking temperatures, keeping bedside
notes, preparing dressings. Soon the doctors forgot their con-
victions that young women were unfit for such work. Though
only six students of the first class remained to graduate, there
were presently so many applicants for admission that the new
superintendent could pick and choose among them.

From 1879 until 1881, Miss Richards was seriously ill and
took an enforced rest. Afterwards she returned to Boston City
Hospital, where she remained until 1885. Under her guidance, the school acquired a then very up-to-date and well-
equipped nurses' home — considerable improvement upon

her own student days when she had to take cat naps in little rooms between the wards.

Linda Richards left Boston to spend five years in Japan, where she taught nursing to young Japanese girls in one of the mission hospitals. Following this period, she returned to her own country to continue service in numerous hospitals, always working to raise the standards of hospital nursing and of nursing education.

After she retired in 1911, friends persuaded her to write her reminiscences and also — all unknown to her — persuaded Dr. Cowles to write a tribute to be included in the introduction.

"The time and circumstances," he wrote, "had created a new opportunity; the way in which Miss Richards met it and used it revealed . . . the greatness of the qualities that made her a leader . . ." He went on at great length to explain and define those qualities, building up a flattering picture of the kind of woman the nursing profession was then producing in greatly increasing numbers and to whom the present profession owes such an incalculable debt.

CHAPTER IX

Nursing in the
Spanish-American War

When Linda Richards reached the age of fifty-seven, her country became involved in a war with Spain. That she does not mention it in her brief *Reminiscences* does not mean that the war did not move her, but it does suggest that, looking back across the years, she did not find it very important in her own nurse's career. In the schools which she directed she had already lived through too many personal battles and was still too deeply involved in "healing disorders of authority." She kept steadily at that work while younger, hardier nurses, many of whom she had had a hand in training, threw themselves into the work of caring for the ill and wounded soldiers. Incidentally, these young women were also fighting their own battles — for official recognition of the place of nurses in the United States Army.

The story of our part in the Spanish-American War is almost as puzzling and as depressing as that of the British in the Crimean. The once glorious Spanish empire that had dominated most of the lands to the south of the Rio Grande was feebly clinging to the last of its overseas possessions, keeping them in subjection by a tariff system that forced them to receive shipments of goods from no other land than Spain. Thus, materials might have to be shipped from New York to Spain in order to be reshipped to Havana, Cuba. This terribly expensive centralization of authority had long been a weakness of the aging empire.

Meanwhile our own country began imposing import duties on Cuban sugar, the chief source of income of the large Cuban landowners. As these faced ruin, laborers lost their jobs and joined bands of insurgents who understood nothing at all about tariffs and imperial policies. Out of work and bitter, their families hungry, they set fire to the sugar plantations of their Spanish masters, who retaliated swiftly and cruelly.

These retaliations were described by our press and were featured as "atrocities," which stirred our own people to a high pitch of righteous indignation. Our government entered official protests and was already well on the road to war when the battleship *Maine* was sunk in Havana Harbor in 1898. How this sinking came about no one will ever be quite certain, but the certain result of the accompanying loss of life of both officers and men was the Spanish-American War.

Like most wars, it brought the victors some profit and much misery — profit in the acquisition from Spain of Puerto Rico and the Philippines and misery in the sufferings of thousands of soldiers, mostly in epidemics that far outlasted the four months' war. Typhoid, that old and vicious enemy, was here reinforced by new enemies, tropical malaria and yellow fever.

As soon as the threat of war became imminent, Anne Williamson, trained in the New York Hospital School of Nursing and graduated in the class of 1896, was all afire to go. Clara Barton of the Red Cross, the idol of her youth and her mother's friend, was the person she naturally turned to. It is a tribute to Miss Barton's agelessness that the young woman took it for granted that her seventy-seven-year-old heroine would be heading immediately for the thick of battle. To her eager young friend's pleas to be allowed to assist on such a mission, Miss Barton replied graciously — and with a caution inspired both by age and a recognition of changed circumstances — that she must wait for "developments" before deciding upon her own course of action.

Not satisfied with this, young Miss Williamson wrote Surgeon General Sternberg, offering her services as a trained nurse. There were then in the country about ten thousand graduate nurses, many of whom followed the same course, only to receive the rather curt reply that there would be no employment for women nurses in the army. The general was even reported as saying that no decent woman would go into army camps — a statement that might have been quoted verbatim from any number of army surgeons, North or South, of thirty-seven years before.

As it turned out, popular attitudes had progressed more than the army surgeons'. As the alerted citizenry learned about unsanitary conditions in army camps, they were able to recognize both that the level of nursing care was needlessly low and the death rate needlessly high. No reasonable preparations, they realized, had been made for tending the victims of a war that had been looming for some months — no plans for enlisting the trained nurses who so much wanted to serve. It was almost as if army doctors shared the age-old superstition that making plans for disaster hastened its advent or, ostrichlike, refused to face the realities that medical corpsmen could not, just because so ordered, discharge the duties of nurses.

Conservative medical officers had no intention of welcoming women into their man's army. Only as violent letters of protest came pouring into Surgeon General Sternberg's office, some even reaching the White House, did matters begin to change. Dr. Sternberg had to acknowledge that the Army Hospital Corps was appallingly short of properly trained and skilled corpsmen and that there was a reserve of trained and skilled women to call upon if he would but give the word. This he soon had to give, and women were freely employed in army hospitals — though it was to take many years and a far more bitter war to establish on a really modern basis the place of women nurses in our army.

On April 12, 1898, war was officially declared against Spain, and by the end of that month Congress authorized the reluctant General Sternberg to employ nurses by contract for the duration of the war. Where these nurses were to come from and how be selected was a matter in which several organizations stood ready to assist the army — the Red Cross, the Daughters of the American Revolution, and some of the rather young professional societies of nurses. The lack of interest of those in charge of army employment of women nurses is shown by the fact that no one agency was given full power.

Of the nearly sixteen hundred women who served in the Army Nurse Corps, the Red Cross, through its Auxiliary Number Three, supplied less than seven hundred. Possibly this was a matter of personalities, for Clara Barton was old and somewhat autocratic and apparently no longer had the influence she once had held in the highest government circles.

The D.A.R., on the other hand, had just the right kind of person in its vice-president, Anita Newcomb McGee, daughter of Admiral Newcomb, with wide acquaintance in official and in military circles. In addition, she was a physician in her own right and could talk with doctors as a professional equal. Dr. McGee had been put in charge of the recently organized D.A.R.'s Hospital Corps Committee and had already drawn up plans for recruiting nurses. It was, thus, completely natural that when she offered her services to the Army Hospital Corps, they should be promptly accepted.

In the course of the war, Dr. McGee passed on nearly eight thousand applications — a remarkably high percentage of the ten thousand graduate nurses in the country. Her standards were up to date in so far as they demanded a diploma from a recognized school of nursing, but they still harked back several decades in her preference for nurses who were neither young nor pretty. Those patriotic souls who wished to become army nurses prepared themselves for their interviews by making themselves appear as plain as possible.

Apparently, however, the screening of nurses was not complete—particularly with those who, enlisting on the West Coast, were urgently needed to help in epidemics that were getting out of hand in Hawaii and the Philippines. One such, without formal nurses' training though with much private experience, addressed enquiries to the Presidio and was told that she might go at her own expense and could probably enlist when reaching Honolulu, where doctors were desperately in need of help. Luckily she turned out to be self-sacrificing and competent, but it is strange that no question seems to have been raised as to her qualifications either before or after she left California. In Honolulu, she was welcomed, told she might go in under contract, and immediately set to work.

This casual attitude toward checking the credentials of one to whose hands was to be entrusted the care of seriously ill men indicates that still, in the year 1898, army surgeons harbored a conviction that all this fussing about nurses' training was just woman's foolishness. To their minds, any willing female with a strong back and a not too sensitive spirit would do quite as well as any other when it came to the grueling and dirty work about army hospitals.

Half the world away from epidemic-ridden Honolulu, Anne Williamson finally won the opportunity of serving in a nearer epidemic. As might have been expected of a friend of Clara Barton's, she entered through the Red Cross Auxiliary. Summoned on July 3, 1898, slightly under three months after the declaration of war but considerably more than that after her first offer of services, she was told she must supply her own uniforms, that the Red Cross would pay all traveling expenses, and that she would receive twenty-five dollars a month while in service. Ideas and salaries had progressed slightly since Civil War days but undoubtedly the cost of living had progressed still more.

Miss Williamson set out immediately for Charleston, where, on July 27, she wrote home lines that might have been taken from the record of a Civil War nurse — save for the fact that this time the nurse had training and hospital experience behind her:

> This morning I was awakened at three o'clock to take charge of a ward in the City Hospital, where there were thirty-seven typhoids. Oh! The suffering is dreadful. The wards remind me of a picture of Dante's Inferno, and the

moans and groans on all sides turn even my experienced nature sick . . . If ever I thanked God for my training it was last night when the ward, in perfect chaos, was turned over to me and I realized that thirty-seven soldiers were looking to me for their comfort and even their lives! [1]

Later Miss Williamson was moved to Chickamauga, where she found conditions in no way better:

. . . Life at Sternberg Hospital was a gruesome business, for the typhoid epidemic was raging and the resultant conditions were more threatening at Chickamauga than in any other area. It became one of the largest fields of activity for Auxiliary No. 3.

The men were brought in by the score. Crowded into ambulances — four and sometimes six at a time; often after a dreadful stretch of hours without water. They were weak and emaciated, their fever-ridden bodies frequently covered by sores encrusted with dead flies; their lips cracked and swollen so that they could hardly swallow. It was a cruel sight — these once strong and brave men struck down by a scourge more fearful than the wounds of battle. The hot, dank, fetid air increased their suffering. Added to this was the almost pitiable lack of everything necessary to their comfort . . .

. . . .

Each day brought more and more sick men, most of them suffering from typhoid and camp dysentery . . . The heat did not let up even at night and temperatures ran high . . . Many of the nurses became ill from hard work, unaccustomed food and long hours. One night when Anne was making her rounds she entered a tent to find the nurse sitting with her head resting on the desk. Anne thought she must have fallen asleep from utter exhaustion . . . On closer examination she saw that the nurse had found her last rest. Like a true soldier, she had remained at her post until death had released her.[1]

[1] *50 Years in Starch.*

Of such stuff were the women made whom General Sternberg had thought unsuited for army service!

Yet even though the trained nurses were ready to work to the point of death, they found themselves constantly hampered by the fact that they had no rank and hence no real authority over the untrained corpsmen they had to direct. Top sergeants liked nothing better than to have a chance of showing their importance and proving their authority.

"The corpsmen resented us before they knew us," wrote Miss M. Estelle Hine, later to become a charter member of the Army Nurse Corps when it was put on a permanent footing. She described her experiences in Manila during the uneasy period following upon the signing of a peace treaty with Spain that left the Philippine Islands in the midst of bloody turmoil.

The hospital was a makeshift affair, inadequately lighted at night by kerosene lamps and candles that added to the almost unbearable heat. And almost as unbearable as the heat were conditions such as those that hampered work in both Honolulu and Charleston. Not the least among these was the old familiar trouble with the medical corps:

> The Commanding Officer had given orders to his doctors that we were civilians and couldn't be held responsible for property. We were to have no authority and the wardmasters were to be kept in charge as previously.
>
> I was assigned to a surgical ward. This was the old Spanish hospital and, although the Americans had hurriedly cleared out much of the rubbish when they took possession, conditions were still deplorable beyond belief. The wards, with a double row of beds through the center and others outside on the porches, accommodated about a hundred patients. The beds were of many varieties. Some were our own folding cots and others consisted of native cane frames placed on wooden or iron horses. The mosquito nets were held up by bamboo

slats, with no two the same size, and the corners were alive with bedbugs.

We watched a good deal and said little those first days . . .

The wounded and sick piled in upon us . . . Often the patients had eaten no food for twenty-four hours on being admitted to the hospital. Nor had some of them had their clothes off for days . . .

It took time and patience on the part of the nurses but we were soon rewarded by being placed in charge of the sick, while corpsmen were responsible for the policing of the wards and for assisting the nurses. Thus, gradually, the Army nurse came into her lawful place. How many tears were shed at night under the mosquito nets will never be known, for always in the morning faces bobbed up smiling.

. . . .

On February 1, 1901, our contracts were annulled and on the very next day we took our appointments for three years' service.

In every way things were bettering for Army nurses. Although the blazing of the trail had been slow and discouraging and much was yet to be accomplished, still we felt we had achieved a good start.[2]

It is a tremendous tribute to the work done by the contract nurses everywhere, to their strength of character, their stamina, their skill, and their sorely tried tact, that General Sternberg was finally sufficiently convinced of the need for women in army hospitals to encourage the creation, by act of Congress, of a permanent Army Nurse Corps. For advice and help in this matter, he turned to Dr. McGee, who had hopefully been making plans for the organization of just such a unit.

Dr. McGee had kept such complete records of the nurses who had served that she understood both the requirements and

[2] Julia O. Flikke, *Nurses in Action.*

the pitfalls of this new corps. She was personally responsible for composing section 19 of the act of February 2, 1901, which gave birth to the Army Nurse Corps. Then, her task finished, Dr. McGee resigned in favor of Mrs. Dita H. Kinney, a graduate of the Massachusetts General Hospital School of Nursing. It was fitting that a nurse should head the Army Nurse Corps, but if a woman physician had not first sponsored it and fought for it, the birth of that corps might well have been delayed many years.

With the coming of peace, the corps shrank to diminutive proportions. Yet, despite the risks, discomforts, and rebuffs of service during the recent war, some women remained to make a career of army nursing. Nearly twenty years were yet to pass before they would receive officer rank and thus be made secure in enforcing their orders over the frequently arrogant top sergeants. Nowadays the lowest rank in the Army Nurse Corps is that of second lieutenant — which even the toughest sergeant has to admit outranks him. Surely not only the nurses but also the army hospitals and, through these, the whole armed forces were to profit by this change.

By the year 1902, the nurses in the army numbered less than two hundred, a total not to be passed again in most of the following fifteen years. They served at general hospitals on various military posts of this continent and, for foreign duty, in the Philippines. Enough to maintain the continuity of the Army Nurse Corps, they were yet too few to cope with any emergency, national or international. Still, their very existence was a tacit admission that the army could expect action — that wars might be a recurrent disaster of the New World even as they had been of the Old, and that nurses would be needed to bind up their wounds.

CHAPTER X

Victory in the Laboratory

Though peace had come, the ancient and unceasing war against disease — notably against those diseases that had all but vanquished the army and the army nurses of 1898 — was not abated. In the course of this new struggle, typhoid was traced to its source and ultimately controlled so that it ceased to be a major menace. Yellow fever was dealt with in its own way — and also tetanus, typhus, and any number of other diseases that fight in all wars as universal enemies.

Applying the same knowledge and skills that had finally shown the way to aseptic surgery, men of science had continued isolating and identifying infecting organisms. They found typhoid bacteria in the intestinal contents of patients ill with the disease and traced those bacteria into drains and sewage.

They knew that uncontrolled water supplies, carelessly guarded milk and foods, and, worst of all, flies that might indiscriminately walk over sewage and food within a few moments — all could be blamed for the spread of the disease. Sanitation and screening would therefore contribute materially towards lessening this spread.

But how to make absolutely certain that all water supplies were unpolluted? How to be sure that flies were always kept away from soldiers' food supplies? The answer had to be found in something more realistic than universal screening — some protection that the soldier might carry within him so that he would be safe wherever duty took him. In other words, he had to be given immunity to the disease.

Immunity itself was no new idea. For a very long time people had recognized that after the ill had once recovered from some of the severest diseases of mankind — smallpox, typhoid, diphtheria, for instance — they need never again worry about infection. And this might be true even though the illness had been in one of its milder forms. Those whose skins were infected with pus from smallpox had far milder cases than those who breathed contaminated air.

To people who had seen and lived in dread of the terrible ravages of smallpox, it seemed a risk worth taking to infect themselves deliberately with pus from active cases so that they might acquire a protective immunity to the more terrible form. As long as two centuries and a half ago, the Reverend Cotton Mather of Boston — more often remembered for his determined witch hunting — was progressive enough to try it on himself and his family and to urge publicly that all others do likewise. And we of this day who take vaccination for granted acquire our immunity through a still milder variant of smallpox called cowpox.

Unfortunately no one knew of a mild or relatively safe form of typhoid fever. But by the 1890's the bacteria had been cultivated in test tubes and studied. Then, in 1897, a Dr. Wright published in England the first paper dealing with a new kind of experimental immunization to typhoid.

The idea back of this was really very simple — once it had been thought of. If those who have harbored typhoid bacteria in their bodies acquire an immunity, could it possibly be that the immunity comes from something in the bacteria themselves? Need a person actually sicken with typhoid to acquire immunity? Might it not just be possible that dead bacteria, properly handled, could produce the same immunity that the living, growing organisms give to the patients in whose bodies they have grown — granting, of course, that the patient has survived? So typhoid bacteria were killed, suspended in sterile salt solution, and injected into human beings. The results we all know, though we may not be conscious nowadays of their importance.

For today typhoid fever is so rare a disease that many practicing physicians have hardly seen a case. Army doctors and nurses no longer have to worry about its menace. Here statistics are dramatic. The incidence of typhoid fever both in our army during the Spanish-American War and in the British army during the Boer War in South Africa in 1899–1902, was about ten per hundred, the death rate being, as always, from 10 to 15 per cent of those infected. The next figures available for the British army after general inoculation during the early days of World War I show a drop in infection to about 2 per cent. And after experimentation had produced a still more effective vaccine by the use of the so-called *paratyphoid* bacteria, the disease was practically abolished as a military hazard for the Allied armies.

As always in such matters, care in the preparation of vaccines and vigilance in the use of them is the price of continued success. During the Second World War the Italian soldiers who had received faulty vaccines showed an 8 to 10 per cent typhoid infection, whereas their British prisoners, protected by the British army's superior vaccines, remained uninfected. And today with antibiotics available to treat the disease wherever encountered, the menace of typhoid has been reduced practically to the vanishing point.

Tropical yellow fever had been another dread killer of the Spanish-American War. Since here again there seemed to be no simple method of acquiring immunity, it became important to trace the progress of the disease from patient to patient — in the hope that somewhere in between it might be tripped up. The strange fact had already been noted that people who had never been in the vicinity of yellow fever sufferers might sicken and die of the disease just as easily as those who had. In fact, those exposed directly to the disease might manage to go scot-free. Was it just bad air or was something carrying the disease from person to person? And what was that something? What, to use a scientific term, was the *vector?*

Almost everyone of our day has heard of the great Dr. Walter Reed, of his brilliant hunch that the carrier was a mosquito, and of his work to prove that hunch beyond the shadow of a doubt. With courage that did not flinch at death, he and his co-workers labored to pin the guilt where it belonged. By 1901 they had accomplished this.

Since at that time immunity could not be safely acquired and the disease was a most merciless killer, control of yellow fever long had to rest upon control of the vector, killing the mosquito where this might most easily be done — in swamps and stagnant pools where it bred. And though the task was no easy one, it was performed so efficiently that yellow fever no longer was a menace in tropical settlements of any size. Finally, during recent years a means of immunization to the disease has been developed.

Thus problems facing nurses of World War I were, on the whole, quite different from those of earlier wars. Antitoxins to cope with tetanus — so terrible a threat of the Civil War — were available. Typhoid was practically abolished. But epidemic influenza was a menace to soldiers and civilians alike. In remote regions such as the Balkans, the typhus which had claimed so many victims during the Crimean War again raised its ugly head. Here doctors could use more modern techniques to pursue and identify the vector in the common body louse. Personal cleanliness amongst troops became more than a fastidious whim.

By the time World War II descended upon an unhappy world, there were few of the more common infectious diseases that had not been controlled. The outstanding medical achievement of that war was the development of antibiotics by the Allies. Beginning with penicillin and continuing through an ever increasing number of new substances — obtained from molds, from fungi in the soil, from herbs once used by our ancestors and since despised and neglected — these antibiotics have built up a remarkable record in the handling of a great variety of infections.

CHAPTER XI

Recognition for the Army Nurse

The nurse's work, though changing with the years and with medical advances, goes on. The same old infections lie in wait to pounce upon the weak or the careless. New ones, or old ones with a new virulence, such as the puzzling hemorrhagic fever of troops in Korea, turn up to challenge doctors, men of science, and nurses. Shell shock — or its modern equivalent — and wounds are still to be dealt with in wars. And surgery, general, orthopedic, or plastic, grows in importance along with man's ingenuity in inventing destructive devices. Finally, there is the ever present question of sickness caused by X rays or radioactive materials.

From one war to the next, the Army Nurse Corps has had

to face this challenge with only a skeleton membership. By the time World War I began in April, 1917, the number of nurses enrolled had reached a bare total of four hundred. Yet thousands were to be needed before that war ended — in fact, before it had well begun.

That this need was filled promptly and adequately was thanks to a roster of available nurses already prepared by a patriotic and foresighted nurse — Jane Arminda Delano, daughter of one of those tragically lost Civil War soldiers. Born in a small upstate New York town, her childhood must have been shadowed by the uncertainty of that word "missing" and colored by the patriotism of those who have sacrificed all, including their own peace of mind, for their country.

As might have been expected in a home torn between the doubts and hopes of a missing soldier's family, the daughter grew up a shy, reserved young girl, attractive but never gay, very earnest about what she wanted to do with her life. A student in a denominational school, she first dreamed of becoming a missionary to other lands. Fate, however, decreed that she should be a nurse and a missionary for the Red Cross Nursing Service in her own land.

In 1884, at the age of twenty-two and after trying her hand at schoolteaching, she finally entered the nursing school at Bellevue Hospital. For more than twenty years after her graduation, she filled a series of positions of increasing importance in the field of nursing. In the year 1909, destiny finally tapped Miss Delano on the shoulder and she entered the Surgeon General's Office as Superintendent of the Army Nurse Corps.

Miss Delano was also at that time chairman of the National Committee on Red Cross Nursing Service, a position which she held without salary for the two and a half years she remained in the Surgeon General's Office — and continued so to hold for the remainder of her life. After she resigned from her army appointment, she worked to bring about the acceptance of the idea that the Red Cross Nursing Service should maintain a reserve of nurses to be called upon by the army as needed in national emergencies. In this she was so successful that, although there were no documents or signed agreements to support it, the War Department many times asserted that the Army Nurse Corps Reserve was to be maintained by the Red Cross. This tradition continued into World War II.

Miss Delano had organized the nursing part of the Red Cross Disaster Service — a service available in floods, fires, or epidemics — so that she had a lengthy list of nurses to draw upon when international disaster threatened. By the time the Armistice was signed in November, 1918, the Army Nurse Corps had swollen to an all-time high of nearly 21,500 members, most of whom had been screened by the American Red Cross.

Anyone trying to study the nursing services of World War I is certain to be completely confused as to where to draw a line between Red Cross nurses and army nurses. It seems to us of this day that one service should have become absorbed in the other; but the army could hardly sink its identity in even so fine an organization as the Red Cross, and Jane Arminda Delano was not a person to encourage the submergence of the Red Cross Nursing Service.

Probably this was for the best, for the relatively young and untried Army Nurse Corps, whose members still carried no rank, had yet to face the demands of a major war. The Red Cross could form a link between harassed military and civilian authorities, could collect funds and expend them where sorely needed without becoming involved in army red tape, and could lend prestige, both national and international, afforded those who worked under the Red Cross of the Geneva Convention.

The Red Cross helped organize fifty base-hospital units for the army and provided equipment for the nurses in these while also maintaining its own separate hospitals — about fourteen military hospitals, as many convalescent homes, clubs and homes for all nurses whether Red Cross or army, plus over thirty hospitals, dispensaries, and infirmaries for the civilian population of France.

Nurses were also at work under other relief agencies. The Rockefeller Foundation financed tuberculosis dispensaries and the American Committee for Devastated France — upon which Mrs. Mary Breckinridge, now of Frontier Nursing Service fame, once worked — undertook an elaborate problem of public health nursing. The details are confusing but the sum is not difficult to arrive at, and it is an impressive one of achievement for American nurses and American organizations.

In peace the Army Nurse Corps again shrank, reaching, in 1935, a peacetime low of six hundred members. Meanwhile, though, things began to look up for nurses in the army. The National Defense Act of 1920 finally conferred upon them the rank of officers.

By the time World War II brought a new upsurge in Army Nurse Corps enrollment, the Red Cross Nursing Service was no longer accepted as the only reserve. There was no bar to direct enrollment — which is no indictment at all of the Red Cross. Today we have a very large and active enrollment in national nurses' organizations which themselves form a natural reserve. Besides, the high standards for graduating and registering nurses in their individual states make it no longer necessary to have those wishing to enroll screened by an intermediate agency like the Red Cross.

By June, 1945, about sixty thousand nurses were on duty with the armed forces in hospitals here and abroad and in front-line stations — even in beleaguered Bataan. Now the trend is to plan fewer hospitals near the battlefields, in which to give only the first stages of treatment and emergency surgery and then fly the injured home for treatment in large, well-equipped military hospitals here in the States. How far we have come since Clara Barton, on her own initiative, brought supplies and help to hospitals set up in deserted farmhouses!

The nurse who joins the armed services today must have a diploma from an accepted school of nursing, be a registered nurse, and be between the ages of twenty-one and forty. She starts in as either a second lieutenant or ensign, depending upon whether she has joined the army or the navy. For the army she must also pass a special mental aptitude test which the navy does not require.

In either service she will wear a neat uniform, specially designed for that service, not dreamed up as a last-minute means of identification. Like all officers, she will have to subject herself to military regulations which may make the rules of her training years look pretty mild.

The army nurse may serve anywhere from base hospitals to front-line stations, whereas the navy nurse may be on a hospital ship or in a naval hospital on shore. To her goes the special responsibility of training hospital corpsmen to serve in situations where women are not accepted — battleships, destroyers, submarines, or isolated and remote naval stations. In 1952 the starting pay was about $325 a month — which should make the $13-a-month Civil War nurse turn in her grave.

An additional reward for the ambitious ones is the possibility of receiving special advanced training at the service's expense. Those, for instance, who might wish to become physiotherapists, dieticians, or anesthesiologists (giving anesthesia in the operating room) may be helped towards this goal while in service so that when they return to civilian life they may continue to follow their interests to positions of greater responsibility and, incidentally, higher financial reward.

An interesting postscript to all this comes in the fact that men nurses are not accepted in the nurses' corps of the armed services and thus are not eligible for commissions. While today increasing numbers of young men are entering schools of nursing as students and continuing their careers as teachers, hospital administrators, specialists in fields such as psychiatric nursing or male nursing, or taking on any of the duties their female counterparts have long assumed — these young men can as yet find no satisfactory place in what was once exclusively a man's army.

In 1950, there were 183 nursing schools accepting men students, all but three of these coeducational. This is quite an advance over the situation in 1920 when the National Defense Act established the Army Nurse Corps. At that time there were only 73 men nursing students in the whole country and these were in men's hospitals, such as Alexian Brothers hospitals. In 1953, there were about 1000 men studying nursing, expecting to graduate and to rise to positions of leadership and responsibility.

No wonder, then, that some of these graduates write articles and letters to nursing journals, plaintively protesting against the unfair sex discrimination of the armed services. They're right, of course — they should be able to hold rank just as women nurses do and not have to serve as uncommissioned medical corpsmen. Yet, sympathetic though we may feel, we cannot help smiling — those of us who have read our nursing history and recall how recently women had to struggle against bitter male opposition to have their skills and training recognized by the armed services. It is thanks to these women that there is now an Army Nurse Corps and certainly no fault of theirs that the Defense Act was so worded as to exclude men.

CHAPTER XII

Schools of the Present

It is to be expected that women will always comprise the majority of nurses and that the number of young men entering nursing schools will remain small compared to the number of young women. Yet the fact that any men are interested in nursing is of utmost significance. Some young women may still incline towards nursing because it has always been accepted as woman's particular talent and because it is a field where male competition has been relatively insignificant. But young men who enter nursing schools can have no such impulses.

When a young man decides upon nursing, it means he has considered a variety of careers and has decided that, despite the fact that nursing has come to be regarded as woman's special field, it is essentially a profession whose opportunities should not be limited by sex. It means that he foresees interesting work and a reasonably satisfactory livelihood for himself and his family. And it should mean he knows that nursing has at last set itself educational standards which entitle it to rank as one of the high professions.

In the eighty-odd years since hospital training of nurses was first inaugurated in this country, nursing education has had its ups and downs — fortunately more ups than downs. It started climbing slowly, for by 1894, twenty-one years after Linda Richards graduated in Boston, the profession which should have been coming of age could boast no more than a total of 500 graduates. In the year 1890, there were no more than 35 training schools in all, yet ten years later there were 432 training schools, with 11,000 young women enrolled as student nurses.

Somewhere between the years 1894 and 1900, doctors and hospital administrators must have come to a realization of the advantages of associating with their hospitals schools which, while training young women for nursing, supplied unpaid workers to the hospital wards — for that is what, in many cases, came to happen. Training schools were springing up everywhere like mushrooms.

Obviously those first 500 nurses graduated by the year 1894 were women of extraordinary character and quality, and, though the content of their formal training would nowadays leave much to be desired, the services they rendered were a revelation to the conservative doctors who soon competed for their assistance. Obviously, too, the so swiftly inaugurated four hundred training schools of the ten years following 1890 could not — even had they wanted to with all earnestness — have produced graduates of equal quality.

Where were experienced instructors to come from? Older nurses, of course! Yet had each one of the women graduated by 1894 been still practicing and been assigned, one each, to the new schools, there would have remained a scant hundred for general-duty work — granting that not one had died or retired and that none were suffering from any interfering duties or illnesses. So these new schools must continually have had to take back as teachers their own relatively inexperienced recent graduates. This need not have been so bad, had there been any fixed standards of nursing education, but as things were much of the education was exploitational.

Partly the students themselves may have been to blame. By the eighteen-nineties — forty years after Florence Nightingale had taken her first determined steps — young women were growing more and more eager to emerge from the overprotection of their nineteenth-century homes and enter worthwhile careers. To many of these nursing seemed the perfect answer — a profession of their own free from male domination yet not too shockingly unfeminine. With clear conscience, they could fight for their right to tend the ill and heal the wounds of the world. So, in rapidly increasing numbers they began clamoring for training which there were too few good schools to supply.

Naturally the fly-by-night schools had good pickings. When those who had the future of the profession at heart managed to get the required training period lengthened to three years, they quite innocently played into the hands of the poorer schools — offering them an extra year of unpaid labor from each hard-worked student who would presently graduate with inadequate preparation for her responsible profession.

This is not, of course, to claim that most of these nurses were poorer in quality than those of thirty years before when one year's training and continuous day and night service were not exceptional. But by 1900, students had a right to expect more. By then a newly graduated Linda Richards would have been looked upon as quite unacceptable in hospitals where experience and her own progressive outlook now made her a competent director. By this time she herself would have been unwilling to graduate a person as untrained as she recognized herself to have been. Progressive, idealistic women were coming to realize what a trained nurse might be and were demanding no less than their ideal.

But to the people who employed nurses, differences between training schools meant little. Graduate nurses were all nurses, and a poor nurse could damage the whole profession. Imagine, if you will, the harm done by a single determined gossip saying, "Oh, those nurses! Why I could tell you things that would make your hair stand on end about that creature who nursed my Janey — hospital graduate, she said, and all that! Next time I'll call in Ma Jones — believe me — she's a *born* nurse!"

Then the next gossip would pass it on in a still more hair-raising version — until Janey Smith would have been practically murdered by some well-meaning woman who had spent three years in a nursing school which overworked and under-trained her.

Naturally the most progressive schools had to do something about this situation before eager young women lost their eagerness for the profession, and before the profession which so many fine women had made so many sacrifices to establish was completely ruined. Standards of nursing education had to be set and State examination and registration of nurses in accord with these standards had to be brought about.

With the passing years and increasing professional opportunities, standards have been raised and schools rated until no one need now accept less than the best in nurses' training — unless, of course, she herself has not the required educational background. Hospital nursing and the instruction that accompanies it is — if forward-looking nurses have their way — on the road to becoming almost as standardized as any other form of higher education, The registered nurse of today is expected to have had so many hours of instruction and served a minimum of so many weeks each on a definite list of hospital services. In general, she should be equipped to instruct as well as do bedside nursing — though for the nurse who intends to make a career of teaching further training is available, and she may end with one or more college degrees as well as her nurse's diploma.

The girl who now enters an accepted school of nursing must have a high school diploma and be of "good character." For the first few months she receives instruction in basic sciences — anatomy, physiology, microbiology, and chemistry — and is taught the basic nursing techniques under the title of "nursing arts." Every nurse has fond memories of the dummy "Mrs. Chase" who is washed, dressed, and tended as no living patient ever was. Then there is the exciting moment when the student is assigned small hospital duties, even to bathing a live patient.

At the end of a few months' apprenticeship comes the momentous capping ceremony, followed by assignment to one hospital service after another until the student has had experience of all kinds of illness and all kinds of patients. The working day is now usually eight hours, as contrasted with the twelve hours expected of earlier nursing students, who were frequently too exhausted in both mind and body to be truly alert and efficient nurses.

Today we are recognizing that there are many routine duties

that can be performed by workers with less elaborate training than that which goes into the three years' nursing course. Many hospitals now run schools for practical nurses — taking in women with less education but often of considerably greater general experience than those who enter the course that leads to an R.N. — Registered Nurse. While there is no bar to the training of young women as practical nurses, older women frequently find in this course a chance to realize a life's dream that limited opportunity or lack of vision denied them when they were young. They receive less classroom instruction than in the regular course and train from nine to eighteen months, when they are ready to go into homes or remain in hospitals, performing less critical and exacting duties than the professionally trained nurse.

Though those outside the profession may continue to marvel at the progress made in nursing education since the days Linda Richards entered upon her training, thoughtful nurses of today are far from contented with their achievements, always reaching to more distant and higher goals. Within recent years they have made, or caused to be made, searching studies of the professional training available to students and of the professional standing of the graduates.

One such study made in 1948 by Esther Lucille Brown of the Russell Sage Foundation, though unhesitatingly frank as to the shortcomings of present-day nursing education, has been accepted with enthusiasm and acted upon wherever possible by nurses eager to raise the standards of their profession. Dr. Brown started in with the question, "Why enter nursing?" asked it in hospitals all over the country, and answered it in her published book. She pointed out the difficulties so often still encountered — in working hours, in salary, in hospital situations where the young nurse finds herself at the bottom of a rigid social structure under a series of older nurses with the medical staff high on top.

From Dr. Brown's lengthy and fascinating study emerge certain outstanding facts. Women still enter nursing because they want to be nurses and because they like people and enjoy helping them. Facing the difficulties, they remain, forever asking, "How may things be bettered? What can we as nurses do about it?"

Today the answer most often is, by continuing to raise the standards of nurse registration and by cutting the poorer schools down to shorter periods of training for "non-professional" nurses, while building up the professional training to include college degrees — Bachelors or ultimately, Masters of Science in Nursing. In our world where college degrees for women have become so commonplace, it seems fitting that the professional nurse should have the above-average background which is identified by a college or university label. For the increasingly complex administrative positions nurses are now required to fill, advanced university training and the degrees that crown such training seem almost necessities.

Long ago this was visualized by those outstanding women of nursing who, in their own lifetimes, have become legends to younger nurses. Today it is impossible to list all of these or even attempt to do justice to any of them, for their greatness will become increasingly clear as the years pass. However, mention should be made of two who are outstanding.

M. Adelaide Nutting, born in Canada in 1858, did not enter nursing school until she was thirty-one. With high cultural background and a brilliant mind, she was able to look far into the future of her chosen profession and resolutely dedicated her life to raising nursing education to university rank. Eventually she herself became a university professor (in Teachers College of Columbia University) and director of the first university department of nursing education in the country.

Annie Warburton Goodrich went still further, believing that a college education should precede nurses' training. Born in the year 1866, she entered training when she was slightly less than twenty-five (then supposed to be the minimum age acceptable). Never wavering in her conviction of the value and dignity of her profession, she strove tirelessly to enhance it. She became dean of the Yale Graduate School of Nursing, where nursing was placed on the same university rank as law or medicine.

CHAPTER XIII

A Teacher of Today

Thanks to women like Adelaide Nutting and Annie W. Goodrich, who entered the still very limited nursing schools of the 1890's but had the vision to see beyond those limitations and the pluck to fight for the realization of their dreams, university nursing schools are now no longer rarities. Women professors of nursing and of subjects allied to nursing have made a place for themselves both in their own first profession of nursing and in their later profession of university teaching.

The successful nurses of our world are women of exceptional character with intelligence sharpened by their training in observing people carefully without letting anyone guess that they are doing so. They learn, first and foremost, to discipline themselves, to be poised, to judge without passion, to work without sparing themselves towards whatever goal, near or distant, they have set their eyes upon.

Because of this, many nurses' life stories read like Cinderella tales. This is not to say that they must start in rags, though they well might, since ability and personality are not determined by outer trappings. Nor do they end in riches — what professional person of our present-day world may hope for riches? But they frequently start in environments limited by accepted tradition — Florence Nightingale was herself an example of this — and end in positions of importance and influence outside their own profession. Lillian Wald, for instance, became so active in matters sociological that many of her admirers accepted her for a sociologist, never knowing that she was, first of all, a nurse.

A typically dramatic life story is that of Estelle Massey Osborne, R.N., B.S., M.A., now assistant professor of education at New York University. Born about fifty years ago in Palestine, Texas, in a South that was yet to become actively education-conscious, she grew up in a home where there were enough children — ten — to give her from the start a fairly wide understanding of human nature. Her mother — a woman of character and insight — was highly education-conscious and determined that all her children should be able to attend college.

Naturally, then, when young Estelle Massey finished at the local high school, she went to a nearby teachers' college whose two-year course prepared for grade-school teaching in her state. After graduating, she taught in a rural Texas school for two years, then moved to St. Louis, Missouri, where her older brother was a successful dentist.

The ambitious girl herself wanted to take up dentistry but her brother — was it professional prejudice or uncanny foresight? — discouraged her and schemed to turn her interests towards nursing. In any case, today he can look at his successful sister with something of a creator's pride and exclaim, "Didn't I tell you so!"

A girl with a college background is always highly acceptable in a nursing school, so Estelle Massey was able to enter the school at St. Louis City Hospital without any delay. She graduated from there in 1924, then spent two years as head nurse on "male medicine." There followed a brief interlude as a St. Louis visiting nurse, after which she went to instruct in a nursing school in Kansas City.

Time and varied contacts had by now taught her the limitations of her own education in a small Southern college and the need of acquiring a wider cultural background. So each summer Estelle Massey traveled to New York to take courses at Teachers College of Columbia University, even though she realized it would take a very long time to acquire sufficient credits for a bachelor's degree.

In the summer of 1929 a chance encounter changed all that. Stopping off on her way to New York for a friendly, casual visit, she went to a dance at which one of her partners asked her if she intended to spend her whole life gathering college credits. She pointed out that she had no alternative — all her extra earnings having gone, in true Massey fashion, to help younger Masseys through school.

"Then," asked the young man, "why don't you apply to the Rosenwald Fund for fellowship aid — they make a point of helping deserving young students."

Knowing nothing about this and feeling very modest on the subject of her own deservingness, Estelle Massey might have discounted the whole idea had not a representative of the fund happened to be in that town at that time. The dancing partner gave her no chance to hesitate but took her to the interview — which resulted in another appointment in New York for a day two weeks later.

It was a trembling young woman who told her tale there, watching eagerly for the tiniest inkling of the interviewer's reaction to her plea. To her this was a matter of terrible importance. If she were to remain in New York for study, she must resign her post in Kansas City by the first of August. If she did not resign by then, honor would bind her to return to teach there whether or not she later was offered the fellowship. But if, once resigned, she did not receive the fellowship, she would be both penniless and jobless.

So she looked hopefully at the poker-faced gentleman whose business it was to listen to pleas such as hers. How many other young people had come to him with their own special tales? How many had better claims for assistance than hers? His calm courtesy told her nothing.

Unable to bear it any longer, she asked tremulously, "Do you think I might have any chance for a fellowship?"

Still poker-faced, the gentleman looked her over. "I think so," was all he would say.

"I think so!" A New Englander might have regarded this as positive assurance but the girl from the Deep South was discouraged. Did his thinking so imply that he was uncertain — that, in truth, he did not expect so and was trying to be gentle about letting the eager young applicant down? It never occurred to the young woman that here was the man who would have the final say.

In due course, but not until after weeks of sobering worry, she was awarded the fellowship and entered Columbia University as a full-time student and candidate for a Bachelor of Science degree, which she received in June, 1930, and followed up with a Master of Arts degree in 1931. Immediately thereafter she went to Washington, where for three years she served as educational director for the Freedmen's Hospital school of nursing. Then the officials of the Rosenwald Fund claimed her as an investigator for a behavioristic study of sharecroppers in her own South.

So Estelle Massey, now a highly educated, highly trained young woman, found herself living in a South far more backward than any she had previously known among strange people whom she must lead to accept her as one of themselves. It is a tribute to her intelligence and adaptability, and to her deep understanding of people — that quality all good nurses must possess — that she succeeded.

Since to a small, remote town every outsider is a foreigner and an investigator an insufferable busybody, she had to conduct her investigation without letting the townspeople become aware of her mission. She was to live in one of their homes, sharing their lives and their interests. The only other educated persons in the village were the schoolteachers, who fled the depressing environment each Friday, not to return before late the following Sunday. But Estelle Massey stayed in the "rurals," making friends with the people, talking with them, sharing their worries, going to their church where they listened to sermons by incredibly ignorant ministers — in fact, sharing their lives down to the last horrifying snake.

Fortunately for her work, she liked people and people, sensing this, liked her. Fortunately also for the people she was the only one among the Rosenwald Fund's imposing array of fourteen investigators — Ph.D.'s, college professors, professional sociologists — who came to the project with any background in health problems. It was she who was able to point out the health handicaps of the underprivileged sharecroppers and the hopelessness of achieving educational or sociological improvement unless one first lifted the terrible burden of illnesses that weighed them down.

How, she asked the at first impatient director of the survey, can you expect a child to take any interest in schooling if he is enfeebled by dysentery or parasitized by hookworm or racked with the recurrent chills and fever of malaria? What if — as she had often found to be the case — he is victimized by all three at the same time? What use, under such circumstances, to offer him advantages he is incapable of enjoying? Unless you do something about his health, you do nothing whatsoever.

The nurse in Estelle Massey would not be silenced and in the end she carried her point. The director listened to her arguments, and it was through recommendations in her reports that mobile health units were finally sent into those areas. But this, Estelle Massey saw, would be only a temporary cure unless the people living there came to understand the why and wherefore of infection. Snakes they could see and cope with, but deadly parasites which they could not see were another matter.

These they must be taught about and no age should be too young for acquiring such information. In fact, the younger the better. They should learn as school children and from their teachers, if possible. So the investigator tried to find out what, if any, health instruction was given in the schools — and found to her horror that the teachers were scarcely better informed than the pupils and their families.

This finally became a problem for teachers' colleges, some of which were ultimately persuaded to install courses that dealt with the basic health problems in areas where their graduates might expect to teach. The nurse-investigator was already becoming a pedagogue.

The nurse-investigator was also human and, in the end, fled those depressing backwoods with their so limited culture and so unlimited varieties of poisonous snakes. She settled first in Akron, Ohio, doing odd jobs for the Rosenwald Fund until, in 1940, she went back to direct her own school in St. Louis, where she remained until 1943. Then she became a consultant with the National Nursing Council for War Service. Here she assisted in interpreting nursing as a career for college students and advised upon improvements in nursing schools in many areas of the United States.

Since 1946, Estelle Massey — now Mrs. Osborne — has been teaching advanced students in the Department of Nursing Education of New York University. One of her courses is entitled "Group Relations," another "Foundations in Nursing"; in both of these she emphasizes the relationships of nurses to one another, to the schools and hospitals where they may work and teach, and to the community in which they live. Her training and background have prepared her well for his — and so successful are these courses that their enrollment must often be limited.

Did I mention that Estelle Massey Osborne is a Negro? Perhaps I should not, for skin color has no deep significance. On the other hand, perhaps I should, for all Negro nurses, from the first one, Mary E. P. Mahoney, who received her diploma in 1879 from the New England Hospital for Women and Children, have had a handicap over and above that borne by other nurses.

Only in 1951 was the National Association for Colored Graduate Nurses — of which Mrs. Osborne had been a longtime president — disbanded and its membership merged in that of the larger, more inclusive American Nurses' Association. In 1948 Mrs. Osborne had been the first Negro nurse elected to the Board of the American Nurses' Association, and served upon it until 1952.

Thus have Negro nurses finally come into their own — their achievements down through the years underlining for all women of the nursing profession how skill and perseverance ultimately triumph against closed doors. From the very start nurses have put their toes into tiny accidental cracks and have kept them there courageously. Then, before the world fully understands what is happening, they walk in proudly, making themselves welcome and even sought after in that world which shortly before had not thought to grant them admittance.

Part Two
HORIZONS

CHAPTER XIV

We Meet Some Students

The word "hospital" brings to mind pictures almost as diverse as human beings themselves. To the ill person, about to enter as a patient, the word often carries the gloomy foreboding of a sentence if not to death then to lengthy and depressing confinement. It is this dread, whether admitted or not, that often keeps the ill away from hospitals. Thus they pass upon themselves severe sentences that might have been commuted to short terms had the illnesses been faced in time.

Why is this still true in days when so many foundations for this or that special medical field are emphasizing the importance of early treatment? Is it the very human dread of the unknown? Possibly so. But is it not also the dark picture of hospital life fixed in the human mind centuries ago, when it was deserved, now maintained by blind tradition? And lest the self-styled enlightened modern become too condescending about this, let her ask herself just what she really thinks of hospitals and what hospitals she thinks about when she talks of them.

Of course anyone who has been a private patient in an endowed hospital will probably be able to recall without loathing and perhaps even with pleasure the days passed in a room with softly tinted walls, furnished with a comfortable chair or so that only visitors sat in, and a mirrored dresser that gave a homey touch even though no patient would expect to have much use for it. There was the patient's own doctor, gravely attentive, and eager young house officers always on hand to be called. And, most of all, there were nurses — competent, friendly, smiling, ready to anticipate the slightest need. Anyone who has been a patient under such conditions is quick enough to praise her hospital.

"Really, my dear, St. Margaret's is wonderful," the ex-patient exclaims with obvious pride in her broadmindedness, "and I do believe I could look forward to going there again — almost." Then she'd spoil it by adding, "But I'd hate to be found dead in one of those awful big city institutions!"

Why do intelligent — or otherwise intelligent — people say that? Why do their friends nod in quick agreement? Are they not really accepting blindly the same ideas that, more than a century ago, drove Mrs. Nightingale and Parthe into hysterics? How many of the people who are so glib in praising one institution and condemning another have had an opportunity to see and understand the inside workings of either? Have any of them a truly just basis for passing judgment?

These are not merely idle questions. They reach to the bottom of the public's attitude toward all hospital and nursing care, and are particularly involved with standards of nursing service and of nursing education. A modern hospital without fine nursing care is as unthinkable as a modern hospital without good doctors. Bricks, mortar, and all the products of the interior decorator's skill are only incidental. A hospital is no better than the care given there. And since equipment is purchasable and doctors are screened elsewhere in the process of their medical education, the really critical question is what the standards of nursing are. In brief, is there a nursing school and how does it rate as compared with other such schools?

"Why is the standard of nursing education in my hospital important?" the uninformed person is likely to ask. "It's nothing in my life, you know, what kind of education high-school graduates are getting there. What I want to know is —"

Yes, what we all want to know is, what kind of care are we or, more especially, our loved ones likely to receive there? And even as we ask this question, we experience a moment of secret horror as we face the fact that we are very ill equipped to judge such matters.

It's really very easy to find out if the hospital we have in mind has a school of nursing and if that school is rated well by the National League for Nursing. If it has been approved, we may know that the nursing service is well run, and that the young people training there are taught basic sciences and nursing skills by competent teachers, many of whom may also be in charge of hospital nursing services. It means that the facilities and equipment of the hospital come within standards set and passed upon by people far beyond the reach of local politics. It means, in short, that the old fear of dirty and degrading charity hospitals need no longer exist.

Actually, beautiful though the private endowed hospital may be and skilled and thoughtful though the care provided, it is the great municipal institutions that really represent the culmination of the century of development started by Florence Nightingale. The most exciting opportunities for training, nursing experience, and human contacts are in the wards of city hospitals, where the wealthy victim of an automobile accident finds no better care than the old and sick and disowned. Even though the one may pay well for his care and the other may be an object of municipal charity, nobody who tends him asks whether this care is to be paid for or how much can be paid. Here, in its highest form, is the healing of wounds, the relief of suffering, and the compassionate care of all.

Center City is a large Midwestern metropolis which was born over a century ago and has been growing ever since, building exclusive residential sections on its outskirts, then engulfing and rejecting them. From the waterfront to the present-day suburbs, one may pass through one section after another of decayed splendor where each large and once showy home with the limited toilet facilities of decades ago now houses many teeming families.

It is near one of these erstwhile residential districts — not the first but possibly the first really pretentious one — that the City Hospital now stands, its tall buildings reaching from the crowded streets to the smoke-grimed sky. And around these tall buildings are the run-down houses and the slum-clearance projects that are the homes of so many to whom the hospital ministers in times of terror, violence, and suffering.

Somewhat apart from the clinic and ward buildings is the nurses' residence where the nurses study, live and have their relaxation. A large lobby leads into the brightly decorated living room, which may become a very gay and lively place when parties are in progress and is never, even in the small hours of the morning, completely deserted. There is a constant ebb and flow as the tide of work bears the young women to and from the main hospital buildings.

Sit down and look at them as they pass and see what manner of people they are. In terms of the past century, they are too young and pretty, too sprightly for the sober weight of the duties they assume. Yet they have a poise and maturity that belies the obvious youth of so many. Some look very fetching indeed in tinted uniforms all but concealed by wide white aprons. Most wear on their heads the proudly won caps. Some are smiling brightly, others are dragging their feet wearily, lines of fatigue etched about their eyes. Looking at them you realize suddenly that young though they may be, they have seen life more whole and more steadily than many a far older person.

Barbara Torrance is one of them — a tall, blonde girl with intelligent eyes and a pleasant smile.

Has she, you ask her, time to talk with you about her profession?

And, although you are convinced that she is really too tired and that there are probably many little personal matters that demand her attention, she nods and says, of course, she always loves to talk about nursing to anyone who will listen.

"How long have you been a student here?" you ask as you recognize from her uniform that she has not yet graduated.

"A year — just."

"And you like it? — if that's not too silly a question."

She smiles and you know she agrees both to your question and your comment. "I love it," she asserts, just in case there may be any uncertainty in your mind.

"Are you one of those girls who always dreamed of being a nurse?"

She smiles again. "Yes and no. I think all little girls go

through periods of thinking of becoming teachers or nurses. I don't think mine lasted longer than most."

"Well, then, what decided you? Your family?"

"Oh, no! They didn't try to influence me in any way — it was my own decision. You see —" she pauses and her face sobers. "Well, about a year before I finished high school I was on a fishing trip with my family and I saw an automobile accident —"

"A bad one?"

She nods but doesn't elaborate and you suddenly understand her reserve. It is not that time and experience have hardened her to tragic scenes, but that they have given her an understanding of all the deeper implications. She has met death too often to treat it lightly.

So you take example from Barbara and wait silently as you watch shadows of a painful memory flit across her face.

"People were badly hurt," she repeats at last, "and I could do nothing — nothing! I felt so utterly useless — I couldn't bear to stay that way . . ."

"That decided you, then?"

"Yes. I knew then that I wanted more than anything else to become a nurse."

"Why this particular hospital — what influenced your choice?"

She looks at you in obvious surprise. "I just never considered any other — I just knew there couldn't be any better —"

Yes, of course, it's one of the best if not one of the most glamorous, you think, as you recall the nearby slums.

"The work's been hard?" you suggest.

"Very hard. Starting right in with our preclinical studies — chemistry and anatomy and physiology and microbiology and pharmacology — so much to master in so little time! But it really was worth while. I mean it gave us a background for our work in the wards — a better understanding, you know. We were capped four months ago."

And you see her, standing tall and straight, proudly lighting a candle of dedication.

"Have things been easier since?"

Again she looks surprised at the ignorance that would permit such a question. "Hardly!" she exclaims with vehemence. "We just never have enough nurses or enough time for all the work that has to be done."

So you draw from her a description of a typical day — up at six, breakfast at six-thirty, starting work at seven with eight hours on duty and a half hour off allowed for lunch. Eight hours of constant work — too few ministering to the too many sick — or valiantly trying to keep awake through doctors' lectures.

"What about night duty?" you ask.

She smiles and assures you that too is coming up soon. When you've been in training school a year, you can expect night duty any time.

"You must have learned a great deal since you've been here," you venture.

She nods.

"Tell me," you go on, "there's been more than just factual knowledge, hasn't there? I mean — well, you meet your high-school classmates now and again, don't you, and talk with them — the ones who have gone into offices, say, or factories and are perhaps drawing bigger wages than you'll get for years. You have no regrets, have you?"

"Of course not. They work — the girls I used to pal around with — but most of them don't seem to get as absorbed in their work as I do. They aren't so satisfied, either — maybe because they have no sense of doing something worth while or of helping people who need it." She pauses, embarrassed at her own vehemence.

"And those people — the ones you take care of — do they appreciate what you do?" you ask quickly, hoping that her embarrassment has not made her too self-conscious.

"That's the best of it," she responds enthusiastically. "They're always so grateful for the smallest things — thanking you as if you were an angel from heaven — and all the time you know you really can do very little —"

While you search about for the next question, she goes on, self-probingly, "Maybe it's that that brings about the greatest change in us. I mean in our attitude towards studying. You see, we use what we learn immediately — and always we know we don't know enough. Maybe the doctor in charge lets something drop or we see something we don't understand written in the patient's chart — and we have to look it up in some book or other — so we'll understand next time. I don't mean anyone says we have to — but we just have to know . . ."

You just have to know! Compassion tempered with knowledge — isn't that the formula for a fine nurse?

"I suppose, then," you suggest tentatively, "that you're looking forward to a college degree some day?"

"Yes — I think all of us would like one sometime. You know, we get college credits for some of the work here."

"Of course." You hesitate, then plunge. "And what about marriage?"

"Oh, that might come in time, but there are lots of nurses who keep on after marriage."

"Well, it certainly should be a good preparation for marriage — nurse's training."

"I couldn't think of any better."

"Then, assuming marriage doesn't interfere, what kind of nursing are you planning to do when you graduate?"

She considers this awhile. "I guess it might be surgical nursing — you see results there and that gives you a lift. But please don't misunderstand — I like nursing — even on those medical services for the old and senile who can hardly remember from one day to the next. They're so touching and so grateful — even if they can't help forgetting . . ."

Such is Barbara Torrance, at one and the same time dedicated and practical, idealistic and unsentimental.

"Is she typical," you ask yourself, "or is it by some quirk of chance that you have been talking to the one student fit to wear the mantle of Florence Nightingale and to carry her lamp?"

So you sit for another while in the lobby and watch the nurses come and go. Then you meet Monica Martin, older than Barbara, slightly plumper, no less pretty. Monica, you can easily surmise, has not, like Barbara, come directly from high school. So you ask her about it and she admits she is very old — older by fully two years than most of her classmates.

"I started out to be a schoolteacher, you know," she explains, "and went two years to a teachers' college. I'd even signed up for grade-school teaching for the following September and was moping around home that summer when Mother suggested that I'd be happier if I filled my time with a job. They needed someone to help in our local hospital —"

"Hospital? How did you happen to choose that? Any special reason?"

"Only that there was the opening and my mother suggested that I try the work. Like most little girls, I'd played at being a nurse and then forgotten it. It didn't mean anything."

"Then what?"

"Then I realized that what I really wanted to be was a nurse. So I resigned from the teaching position and called up the director here and arranged for an interview . . ."

"How long ago was that?"

"Two years—I've another year to go, you know."

"Well, you wasted quite a lot of time on teachers' training, didn't you? Are you sorry about that?"

"Oh, it wasn't wasted time at all. It helped a lot — when I have to write up case studies and when I have to present them, I don't have to grope for words. And then when it comes to teaching patients about personal care—well, the speech training I had helps and I think maybe it helps to be a little older . . ."

"And you've never regretted coming here — surely school-teaching wouldn't have been so exhausting?"

"I wouldn't change for the world. Oh, there are times one gets discouraged and thinks about quitting but one never does. Those who can't take it drop out early and it's a good thing they do. Because you've got to feel a satisfaction in the work that will carry you through those moments of awful fatigue . . ."

"When you finish training — what then? You must have done some thinking about that."

"Of course. Well, I'd like to get my credits together and fill out the requirements for a B.S. in nursing at some university. Then maybe I could teach on the faculty of some school of nursing—"

"You mean you don't want to do bedside nursing yourself?"

"On the contrary, I want to combine it with teaching. I love the contact with the patients here — people from all walks of life and with every imaginable illness. I wouldn't want to give it up. I could do ward teaching, maybe. I've had some small experience in that—we seniors have to help instruct the newer students, you see."

Yes, one sees. One sees the teacher and nurse developing together and a future of widening influence and increasing usefulness for both.

"You must have been here long enough to have tried most of the services. Which of them do you like best?"

She grows thoughtful. "Well, once I thought of becoming a psychiatric nurse but I'm not so sure now. I think maybe I like surgery as well as anything."

"It's more dramatic, isn't it?" you ask as you remember the things Barbara told you. "And I suppose you like to see results?"

"Yes, that's so."

"But I'd think the operating room would be terribly exhausting."

"Oh, that's a separate service. 'Surgery' means before and after the operation — the care of the patients."

"And what about the medical services," you probe, "the chronic patients, for instance? Don't they tell us that with modern methods of combating acute infections we're going to get more and more chronic illnesses in hospitals? How about those patients — don't you find them depressing?"

"You can't help getting discouraged sometimes but you can grow awfully fond of those folks — so many of them old and lonely. They need human contacts so and they're so pitifully grateful for the least thing you do —"

At your urging, she goes on listing the other services — communicable diseases, tuberculosis, obstetrics, and so on. When she mentions pediatrics, you know by the tone of her voice that she has some special feeling for it and for the young children she has tended. You know, too, that she will always be ready to follow her chosen profession into whatever situations, cheerful or gloomy, fate may call her.

An alert little person with a diamond and a wedding ring on her left hand comes by. Here, you think, may be someone who will tell you the other side — someone who is giving up nursing for a life of domesticity. Though, if her rejection were complete, you suddenly realize, she would not be here at all. She is Mrs. Martha Hemingway, glad, like her fellow workers, to talk about the work that during recent years has absorbed so much of her time and thoughts.

Yes, she murmurs in answer to your first question, she always knew what she wanted — can't, in fact, recall when she was not determined to become a nurse. And she selected her school carefully, for she wanted to become a fine nurse. No, she's never regretted her decision. How could she?

"But you're married — doesn't that mean you're giving it up?"

"Oh, no! I'd always find some nursing to do, you know, wherever I was. But I shan't have any worries about that — my husband is entering the missionary field and I'm going with him — there'll be plenty of nursing to do there, I'm sure."

"That sounds as if you might be interested in public health work."

"Yes, I think I'd like it. But we don't get much of that as students. You take special training later if you want to go into that field."

"Then what is your favorite work here?"

She considers the matter gravely. "I think maybe it is operating room and the emergency work. It's the most exciting and the most challenging. Often there isn't too much you can do, but it may count terribly. And in the operating room you're on your toes all the time. It's definite and so — so important and it gives one such a sense of achievement."

"What about the medical wards — that must seem rather dreary routine to you."

"Well, it's not a bit exciting," she admits. "It's just the same routine over and over. But if you like people, you want to make them comfortable and happy."

"What about pediatrics?"

"Oh, I liked that — particularly at night with all but the sickest babies sleeping and a sort of hushed peace over the place. Then the new ones that are brought in are so very sick and one can do so much . . ."

"It's quite obvious you enjoy the work," you remark, "and so do the others I just talked to. Yet it's hard to believe that no one here finds shortcomings in the training. It doesn't seem human."

"Oh, we're human enough," she insists promptly, "and if you ask for gripes, you'll get plenty. I can even contribute a few of my own. For my part, I could often do with more convenient hours, more time allowed for professional reading and essential studies, more time to give to individual patients not only so that they'd get better care but so that I'd really learn from my work. Now I'm so driven it's positively frustrating . . ."

"Then it's fundamentally the old need for more nurses?"

"Partly. But not entirely. Nursing education, I think, should be treated like any other form of advanced training. But we'd need a different attitude on the part of a lot of doctors and hospital administrators and even — some of our own nursing instructors. Though as I see my own instructing days looming ahead, I sort of begin to understand the difficulties they're laboring under."

"Such as?" you urge.

"Well, I don't think all of them have all the training and experience they could use. And when they do have it they're not always recognized for the highly trained professional people they are. For that matter, neither is it very generally recognized that we undergraduates are professional students, like medical or law students."

"Then — if I may ask a tactless question — why do you stick with it? Surely there are other interesting and more profitable things to do."

"But we like it! It was you who asked for gripes. We'd all have quit long ago if we didn't like it. Of course we're going to do something about it, though. Look what's been done in less than a century!"

CHAPTER XV

Work in the Wards

Mrs. Hemingway is already a senior with but a few days lacking to complete her required residence. She's been through every service and knows the hospital well. So you ask her hopefully if she's willing to show you around the hospital. And she answers quickly, "Of course, with the director's permission."

But you're already armed with that. Without it, you'd hardly be making yourself at home in the nurses' residence.

Together you walk across the hospital grounds and enter one of the tall buildings. It's a big place because it has to be and the corridors are long. Floors are polished stone and the walls are a soft green. There's no attempt at adornment that is costly to apply, costlier to maintain. Each ward patient, you note, has

a bed and bedside stand and perhaps a chair. That is all that
is necessary there — or in any hospital, for that matter. The
rest is that invisible, vital something called nursing care.

"Where shall we start?" your guide asks you, and since you
know nothing at all about it you reply, flippantly:

"Why not start with the cradle?"

So she rings for the elevator. You step out into the pediatrics
division, with the same long corridor and the same light green
walls. Only here the solemnity is relieved by the presence of
one little tot, running happily along on bare feet, his shapeless hospital nightgown — affectionately called a "johnny" —
billowing out behind him to leave exposed most of the skinny
little boy beneath.

"Isn't he too sick for that?" you ask in maternal alarm.
"Shouldn't he be in bed?"

Your guide smiles sadly. "Oh, if he's running around it's all
right for him to. He probably needs exercise. Probably there's
nothing wrong with him now — only that his folks haven't
turned up to claim him."

"You mean people actually desert their children here!" you
exclaim in horror.

"One never knows," she murmurs, "what has happened —
whether it's accident or intentional. Their folks may turn up
any time to claim them — only sometimes it's awfully long —
and sometimes their folks disappear completely . . . We take
as much care of them as we can but we never have time for the
sort of personal attention and warm affection that a little child
really needs . . . It's just not right . . ."

No, of course it's not right, you agree, shocked at learning a
bit of that seamy side that all these young women have constantly to face.

You move into a little ward whose eight cribs are strangely

still. Drawing closer, you perceive with shock that here are the babes rejected because of deformities — poor little ones condemned to brief and tortured lives, cared for here with exquisite gentleness. And in the ward beyond are a couple of cribs holding babies afflicted with degenerative diseases. All the progress and inventions of modern medical science cannot do more than prolong their lives briefly. But in caring for them doctors and nurses may learn something that may help to ease the lives of others similarly afflicted.

With a sense of relief you move on to those who have nothing more incurable than a badly bruised shin or a broken nose, those who have just parted with tonsils or appendices — or even those who have been isolated because of some communicable disease beyond the completely successful reach of antibiotics.

You go up to the next division on the floor above. Even before you open the elevator door, the echoing babel reaches your ears.

"Watch out," your guide warns cheerfully, "or these kids may tear the clothes off you."

The elevator door opens to reveal you to a group of mischievous-eyed children from, say, five to eight years of age. They're all clad in hospital johnnies, all show the same hospital pallor — but there's really nothing uniform about them. In the instant before you step out, you know they're taking you in and sizing you up and, recalling your guide's warning, you clutch yourself a bit closer.

But they don't pounce upon you. They just let out a series of bloodcurdling whoops and go scampering off down that fascinatingly long corridor. All save one, that is — a grinning lad of about five who comes up to you and offers his hand in a gesture doubly appealing in one of so impish an appearance. His cheeks show the usual pallor but you know that underneath is the Lone Ranger or Superman. You take his hand and walk with him down the corridor. Then, just as you begin to grow a bit misty-eyed about him, he withdraws his hand as inexplicably as he offered it and goes scampering after his playmates.

Here again you can glance into rows of little wards, each with its quota of small beds, most of them still occupied. A small attempt at decoration has been made by applying colorful holiday motifs to walls and windows. At the end of the corridor is a cheerful sun parlor.

Here two youngsters are playing checkers. One of them has a leg in a cast, the other, much bandaged, explains cheerfully that he played with some gasoline. Yes, of course he knows better — now. Weeks of skin grafting are a pretty grim teacher.

As with the infants below, there are here all kinds of children with all kinds of troubles, as the echoing corridors remind you. This is no place of stern quiet, and you are glad it is not — though the nurses may often wearily think otherwise. Somehow they manage to smile with unruffled calm and get done the things that have to be done.

Obstetrics is your next port of call. This, you are thankful to note, is not a place of either illness or sadness. The patients sit about in small groups, chatting quietly. Here is the "rooming-in" section — where the hospital tries to duplicate the home by keeping mothers and babies together from the start, letting the mothers watch and tend their babies as much as they can. But if the mothers prefer complete rest, there is also the older system of keeping the babies apart in rows of tiny cribs in the nursery where the nurses wash them and tend them until time for feeding.

Across the hall is the carefully guarded room which contains the incubators for premature infants. You can see these tiny creatures through several thicknesses of glass — incredibly small to be alive and incredibly perfect for beings so small, little hands and feet wriggling with flawless articulation or resting quietly in sleep.

A supervisor and a couple of student nurses are on duty. At the moment there is no woman in labor and quiet pervades the place. The nurses can take time to show you around — the delivery rooms, with their equipment ever ready for mothers that may be brought in with no margin of time, the waiting bassinets, the great piles of clean linen upon empty beds, waiting to be sorted, put away, used, washed, and sorted again in a cycle that ends only as each piece wears out.

"Wouldn't you like a cup of coffee?" one of the nurses offers suddenly, and you look at their weary faces and realize that they need coffee far more than you.

So you murmur, "Why, yes, if you happen to have any."

They lead you into a small room whose walls are lined with shelves of equipment. On a table is a two-burner electric stove upon which is a steaming white enameled hospital pitcher, emitting a most tempting odor. One nurse reaches down five thick white cups and fills them from the pitcher. Cream in a dairy bottle and sugar in a glass jar and an assortment of teaspoons complete the service. It's all informal — one sitting on the only chair, two perched on stools, one leaning against the edge of the table and another against the wall. In the air is that blessed relaxation that goes with a consciousness of a temporary lull in pressing duties.

It's easy here to ask them questions — the old one, for instance — as to why they went into nursing. And they give the same answers — I just never thought of anything else; or, I don't know really, it just seemed the thing for me to do; or, it's hard to decide what the motive really was, I've never thought it out, but it seemed what I'd always wanted to do.

One, a little older, smiles quietly and you press her for her answer. She is one of those girls who wants to be a missionary and feels that care of suffering bodies will minister best to souls. Her plans have been carefully laid — training in public health nursing, then work on Indian reservations where she knows that there is great need for bedside nursing, hospital administration, and the teaching of nursing techniques to Indian girls.

"You like it?" You ask the same old question of no one in particular.

"Of course. If I didn't I'd have quit almost as soon as I started."

"No regrets, then?"

"Of course not. There's nothing in it unless you love it."

"Don't tell me there haven't been any bad moments!"

"Oh, but of course."

"Such as?" you probe.

"That awful first moment when I'd just gotten on ward duty and found I was expected to bathe my first patient. It was terrible. I felt like a new mother with her baby — as if he were going to break — and I knew he knew more about it than I and that he'd know everything I did wrong. And of course I knew I'd do everything wrong."

"And did you?"

She smiles reflectively. "Practically — but one survives, after all — and the patient, too, wonder of wonders. The first time's always that way, I guess —"

The others nod in agreement.

"Well, was that the last of the bad moments?" You look around the group questioningly.

Another speaks up. "Then there's that first time you go on

night duty and find you're alone and in charge of a big ward, responsible for any number of sick people. If anything happens, you'll feel almost like a murderess because it's all your responsibility and you're sure you'll never be able to do the right thing . . ."

Again the others nod and you realize that this is a universal experience of nursing students.

"And then an emergency arises and you just haven't time to think," she goes on reflectively. "You just have to act—"

"Yes?" you urge gently.

"And when it's all over you find you haven't done as badly as you feared and you know you can do it— and you feel as if you'd come into a million —"

A million! At least! Isn't a chance to learn their own strength a priceless gift to the young?

You move on to Division Twelve where are rows of beds filled with older women, their wispy gray hair accentuating the hospital pallor on wrinkled cheeks that will never again glow with youth. Your guide stoops to exchange a friendly word with a woman who is busily trying to untangle a skein of string, as if the difficulties of life itself were to be solved thereby. She looks up and smiles happily, answering in a thin cracked voice. In a nearby bed another woman groans hopefully, trying to attract to herself a bit of the attention being squandered on her neighbor. Your guide gives her the warm smile and kind word she craves.

Old age presents problems that nursing will not eliminate — but compassionate understanding such as shown by the young woman walking beside you will certainly help make them less grim.

CHAPTER XVI

Place of Light

Beyond doors that close after you with a startling swish of finality is that area where only the initiated few may penetrate when well and fully conscious. This is the operating-room floor, alternately humming with the subdued noise of its feverish activity and dropping back into quiet, secure in the confidence of being prepared for emergency. Here the hazards of everyday living may, without forewarning, bring any of us. Upon the preparedness of this place may hang the lives of those whom we hold dear.

Miss Julia Rentner is in charge of the operating room. Will she talk with you? Yes, for luckily there is no operation coming

up immediately. The day's op schedule — "operation schedule," she explains with a smile — is completed and they've just
finished an unscheduled emergency operation on a broken
nose. She gestures towards the room where that was performed
and you step hesitatingly inside the doorway, because in your
heart you feel that surgery performs miracles of healing and
that the place of this performance deserves an awed respect.

It is a high, clean room, its walls lined with soft green tile
to the height of a man's head, painted in a still softer green
on the walls above and on the ceiling. From the center of the
ceiling hangs an elaborate fixture of lights and mirrors, so con-
trived that light may be concentrated upon the spot where most
needed and delicately counterpoised so that it may be set at
any height. And that is all. From tiled floor to ceiling, from
wall to wall, there remains no evidence of the use to which the
room has so recently been put — save for the moisture that
suggests a barely completed scrubbing. Operating table, anes-
thetics, instruments — all have been wheeled out to be checked
over and prepared for the next emergency. The page of life
written here has been forever turned. The next lies open and
clean for the writing.

"In this kind of hospital," Miss Rentner explains, "we get
all kinds of emergency operations and have to be ready to take
care of any emergency on practically no notice."

"*Any* emergency?" you repeat unbelievingly.

Miss Rentner smiles with quiet pride. "Any," she repeats
firmly. "We figure we can be ready for any operation in fifteen minutes to half an hour. Come, I'll show you . . ."

She leads you into a room lined with cabinets and glass-
front cases from floor to ceiling. A young student nurse and
an older attendant are working here with quiet assurance.
Miss Rentner introduces them and you realize that here for

the first time you are meeting not only a student but also a hospital-trained practical nurse.

At your question, the older woman smiles with pleasure, "Yes, I always wanted to be a nurse — but couldn't manage it when I was young. Now I'm doing just what I wanted to. I can't tell you what a privilege it is for me . . ." And all the time she keeps her hands busy sorting fantastically shaped steel instruments.

Miss Rentner's eyes follow your inquiring glance. "Those are the surgical instruments," she explains. "Here the hospital owns practically all that are used. In private hospitals, you know, each surgeon has to have his own —"

"It sounds confusing — having to keep each man's apart. Sorting them out here looks bad enough."

"Oh, we get used to it. Sometimes our surgeons have their own pet instruments — so they bring them in and we sterilize them and have them ready for them."

"What are those?" you ask, pointing at random towards the table.

She picks one up. "This is a retractor for holding an abdominal wound open so the surgeon can work freely inside — and here's what we call a hemostat," she adds, picking up something that looks like a cross between scissors and pliers; "this is for clamping off exposed blood vessels —"

She notices your startled expression and explains swiftly, "Oh, you mustn't think surgery is bloody. It isn't one bit. The patient's all covered up with sheets except for the small area where the operation is going on and that small area is simply bristling with hemostats and packed with sponges, so you hardly see any blood at all."

"Sounds as if it might be hard to remember that there is a real person underneath," you suggest.

"We're always conscious of that — of the real person there who needs surgery — to whom, perhaps, surgery may be a matter of life or death. And the anesthetist never lets us forget — always watching pulse and respiration. Surgery's very exciting, and it demands everything you have — but when it's over you have a real sense of achievement . . ."

You turn back to the cases and stare fascinated at the hundreds of articles that go into preparation for a surgical operation.

"How in the world," you ask, "do you know what you must have ready for each operation? And just what does 'getting ready' mean?"

"Well, to begin with, there's tomorrow's op schedule posted on each operating-room bulletin board. So we know the kinds of operations to plan for and when, and we have a list of the articles required for each." She hands you a sheet of paper headed "laparotomy" with a long list of instruments and articles beneath. "So we count them out and tie them up in packages —"

She picks up a lumpy cloth-wrapped package. From its weight, you know it must contain many steel instruments.

"Then," she goes on, "we mark it with indelible pencil — contents and date — and put it into a sterilizer along with other packages of instruments and linens —" she points to a great shining circular steel door reinforced with spokes of steel and adorned with fascinating gauges. "We put it in here under high pressure of live steam just as you might in your own pressure cooker and leave it in for fifteen minutes. That makes things sterile — kills the germs, if you want to put it that way. Meanwhile the indelible pencil turns purple so we never have any doubt whether the package has been sterilized or not."

Shades of Sir Joseph Lister! The world surely has come a long, long way!

"Well," you ask, "so that gets ready for the scheduled ops. What about the emergencies — how do you prepare for them?"

"We have to keep sterile packages ready — a large one for abdominal operations in general and smaller ones to adapt the large ones to special requirements. We can keep them on hand or we can sterilize them as needed. It takes more than fifteen minutes to get a patient scrubbed and prepared for an operation — so we're always ready as soon as the patient is."

"Then a nurse is always on duty here?"

"Yes. And others on call to be here in a few moments as needed." She laughs a little and adds, "Some nights they never get away."

You move on down the hall and she points out several more operating rooms with shelves and tables and bulletin boards listing the next day's op schedule, the types of anesthesia desired by the surgeon in charge, and any special extra notations that may be needed. In the ceilings of two are large glassed-in domes where, so your guide tells you, people may sit to watch operations.

"Might I?" you ask quickly.

"If you have the right permissions."

So you make up your mind to get them and return on the morrow.

You start back along the hall and notice a smaller room with a couple of operating tables with something like huge boxes underneath.

"That's the cast room," your guide explains, "for putting plaster casts on orthopedic cases —"

"And those buckets at the corners — what are they for?"

"For dipping the gauze in water." She leads you into the

room and picks up a roll of gauze from which a fine white powder sifts down onto the floor. "See, this is already impregnated with plaster of Paris. The doctor just dips it and winds it on. It sets as it dries."

"Mighty clever! And this?" You point to something that looks like a large empty photograph frame.

"That's for the X rays. The doctor watches every detail as he works so there's no fumbling. He just orders as many pictures as he thinks necessary and the X-ray technician comes up and takes them and develops them in the darkroom next door. Then they're put into the frame for examination —"

"You don't overlook anything here, do you?"

"Not if we can help it."

While an operation is in progress, the bare, high-walled operating room becomes filled with equipment and people, its atmosphere electric with the drama being enacted. From the glassed-in dome above, you are a spectator . . .

Here, says the op schedule, is the victim of an accident, picked up some days ago in the street where he had fallen, lying unconscious because of injury to his head. Had someone struck him and for what reason? Or had he stumbled and fallen and hurt his head against the curb? What was his history? Who was he? Only the papers in his pocket give a clue and papers can lie. A nobody, perhaps. Or perhaps not. But today, all unconscious, he is served by a great neurosurgeon, two assisting surgeons, an anesthetist, and three nurses — one of those incredibly rich poor human beings who is coming into his inheritance of decades of progress in scientific knowledge and surgical techniques and in the art and practice of nursing.

You look down at the operating table, strait and narrow like the gate to eternal life, and see there the vaguest outlines of a human figure swathed in sheets of green cloth whose varying intensities of color testify to the varying numbers of times they have been put through laundry and steam sterilizer. From head to foot he is covered, the only visible evidence of the man below being the tips of his feet, one of which quivers spasmodically, and an area revealed by a slit in the sheet over his head.

Above the level of his chest and across it is a tray, also draped, that looks grotesquely like the trays from which bedridden invalids are fed. But here the fare is grimmer — rows of gleaming forceps and hemostats and scalpels of various sizes, a cup or two of liquid which your guide tells you is a sterile saline solution, and some oddly shaped polished steel instruments strangely resembling carpenters' augers.

Since, because of the type of injury, this operation must penetrate the patient's skull, the surgeons are grouped about the patient's head — each one clad in a bulky green robe tied in back at the neck and waistline. Nowadays, to avoid glare, green is the color favored in operating rooms. Upon the surgeons' heads are close-fitting turbanlike caps and masks of gauze to hold back any germs that might be in the breathed-out air. Their hands are covered with rubber gloves so tightly fitting and so thin that one hardly notices them save for the folds that come up over the cuffs of the gowns and the curious yellow tint they lend to the hands they encase. Upon this thin protection and upon his own knowledge and skill, the surgeon may be gambling not only the patient's but also his own health.

Two nurses, similarly gowned and gloved — their sex to be guessed at only in their slimmer build and slighter stature — stand at the level of the patient's chest. The nurse-anesthetist, in white but masked and capped like the others, sits on a stool, presiding over a bewildering array of colored tanks, shining steel handles, gauges, washing bottles, and rubber tubes. Hers, you are told, is the fearfully responsible task of giving the anesthetic — just the right amount, neither too much nor too little — watching the pulse and breathing of the patient, deciding if it is necessary to give oxygen. Keeping jealous guard over life, she must reach almost blindly under the drapery and tray of instruments.

A third operating-room nurse, also in white, also capped and masked, moves freely about the room, forming a connecting link between the sterile team about the table and the outside hospital world. She, your guide tells you, is the circulating nurse — hers the responsible judgment that makes sure supplies are brought in as needed and delivered in a still sterile condition to those who must use them or pass them on to the surgeon. Here is a chain from nonsterile to sterile that must not be broken if the patient is to have a fair chance of survival. Of all the progress a century has brought, this is not the least. Surely the spirit of Sir Joseph Lister must haunt such places ecstatically, and perhaps a little enviously.

"I guess I understand about sterilizing instruments and linens," you remark to your guide, "but precisely what is meant by sterility when you talk of the doctors and nurses? How can people put on sterilized gowns and still keep them sterile?"

"You have to be scrubbed before you touch them — and it's a long, tiresome process. Think of scrubbing your hands for three minutes in a mixture of detergent and germicide, then time out for cleaning nails, then another four minutes of scrubbing."

"Whew! Any skin left after that?"

"Some."

"Then what?"

"Then you manage to put on sterile gown and gloves without contaminating them. Some nonsterile assistant ties you in back, and then if you need to have a sterile back also, someone with sterile hands pins a sterile towel over your gown."

"It must look awfully fetching," you comment flippantly as you look at the already rather shapeless figures below busily conferring upon some matter you'd very much like to be able to overhear.

She smiles again.

"Do the surgeons go through the same routine?" you ask.

"Naturally — only the scrub nurses help them into gloves and gowns."

"And masks and caps, too?"

"Oh, they're not sterile — they're put on before scrubbing begins. We keep them on most of the time, as maybe you've noticed."

"It sort of makes you all look like nuns."

Down below, the conference has come to an end, and as the chief surgeon reaches his hand towards a scalpel, you know this is the zero hour. He draws the scalpel swiftly across the revealed skin and a thin red line follows. Do you imagine it, or is there a tenseness that communicates itself through the many feet of air and the thick panes of glass that separate you from the scene below?

One of the nurses in green has already picked up instruments to hand to the surgeon. The other turns briefly towards a great curved table behind her, spread with row upon row of gleaming surgical instruments. From her position she can reach out to touch almost any article there or, with a slight

step, take from the drum close by any sterile linens that may
be needed. At her elbow is a container full of little sponges
that are to be used presently. The circulating nurse stands
attentively at a little distance to one side.

The center of all this activity is now the chief surgeon. Each
time he moves, he sets off a widening wave of motion in his
assisting surgeons, in the scrub nurses, reaching finally to the
circulating nurse, who moves about in a general activity that
is carefully timed and planned, bringing things in, taking
some out, or, with a lull at the operating table, pouring sterile
water from a steel pitcher into a matching sterile basin. Here,
if necessary, sterile gloved hands may be rinsed without break-
ing the chain of sterility.

In mounting excitement you watch as, layer by layer, the
surgeon carefully opens the incision, using tiny metal clips
that one of the nurses holds in readiness for his reaching
hands. The other nurse is preparing little squares of cloth
sponges and strips of some highly absorbent material, dipping
them in a sterile salt solution, drawing them expertly between
her fingers to remove excess moisture, laying them out on the
back of her hand for the surgeon to pick up as needed.

The minutes tick by and mount up. Now the surgeon reaches
for the auger and is drilling a tiny hole in the skull. Now he
enlarges it cautiously. The anesthetist reaches a hand towards
the green oxygen tank. The scrub nurses work continuously
with the economy of effort necessary in an operation that may
go on and on.

Though you may know nothing at all about surgery and
though this may be the first and possibly the last time you are
permitted to sit in as an interested spectator of a tremendous
drama of life and death like that enacted below, you sense that
here is a well-integrated team, acknowledging authority, an-

ticipating orders, recognizing the rules by which all teams must function. No wonder those who work in operating rooms feel a deep satisfaction in their work.

A few have left records of their reactions to this environment. One of these is Mrs. Mary Williams Brinton, who in her book *My Cap and My Cape* describes her training as an anesthetist some twenty-odd years ago, and her work as such in the operating room:

> . . . After several months' vacation, I enrolled in a class for the study of anesthesia under the famous Dr. Edward Beach at the Howard Hospital, then standing on South Broad Street. This specialty had always attracted me because it sharpened powers of perception and enhanced the ability to recognize symptomatic changes, but I feared it, realizing that it flirted with life and death.
>
> .   .   .   .
>
> I went for further study to the Deaver Clinic in the Lankenau Hospital where Dr. John Deaver enjoyed a worldwide reputation due to his professional skill and power of demonstration. The days there were colorful and still vivid. The supervising nurses, Lutheran Deaconesses, were picturesque in lawn caps, tied under the chin, that spread fan-shape to their shoulders. They moved as if on wheels, were extraordinarily clever, and had a thorough efficiency obtained from years of work with the Professor, as they called Dr. Deaver.
>
> The amphitheatre where he performed was of white marble with tiers of seats like the Colosseum around the side. The operating table stood in the center, and near it trays of instruments covered with white cloths. On clinic days, the room was filled with medical students, and doctors registered in the visitors' book from all over the world. Anyone of prominence in the profession sooner or later put in an appearance. They watched the preliminaries intently, as silently the Sisters flitted about, bringing a sense of impending drama, a perfect build-up for the Professor's arrival.

When he entered he gave the impression of a great actor
on opening night, his waxed moustache heightening his the-
atrical effect. He wore high tan boots, white operating pants,
a sleeveless undershirt and over all a long gown. His introductory remarks smacked with sarcasm and humor; their import climaxed as the sterile gloves were slipped on his tremendous hands, and he took up the scalpel.

He operated carefully and without hesitation, keeping up
an amusing flow of conversation, all the while intent on what
he was doing. I had heard it said that he felt more at home
in the peritoneal cavity of humans than any other surgeon,
and I easily believed this as I watched the quick sureness of
his hands which moved as if guided, and the ease with which
he explored the belly. It made me feel I was in the presence
of greatness.

. . . .

When chloroform was given, he was apt to administer it
himself. I can see him pouring it on a piece of gauze, com-
menting on the technique as he went along. It was during
these demonstrations that I learned to use it.

Dr. Deaver, to a newcomer, was terrifying; he consist-
ently tried to rattle me. How I envied the cool precision and
steady nerves of Miss Rapp, his anesthetist! As the work became familiar, he trusted me to give anesthesia unaided.

. . . .

. . . As I watched the intent faces of the audience and realized the far-reaching gift to humanity of this man, I felt over-
whelmed at being a part of his operating team. A strange ex-
ultation filled me, for in my inexperienced way I was partici-
pating in healing in its highest form . . .

What a very great distance surgery had come since those
"amputating rooms" of Civil War days from under the doors
of which blood flowed in streams!

CHAPTER XVII

Clothes and the Man

From medical wards and operating room to clinic is a long, long way, even though the clinic is housed in the farther corner of the same great group of buildings.

No matter how skilled the nursing, the patients in the wards are bound to have a sense of rejection by the outside world. They are living, for a longer or shorter period, removed from family and friends in an artificial world of identical beds filled with almost identical patients. Each, to be sure, has his special illness, chronic or acute, his regularly satisfied needs for the ministrations of doctor or nurse, and his too rarely satisfied need for some gesture of personal affection that might set him apart from his neighbors and make of him an individual human being.

To the clinic come those whose ties with the world outside the hospital walls are still stronger than the bonds of illness.

With them comes that outside world, demanding recognition of its pulls and its problems. Some of those problems may have caused or aggravated the illness but, no matter how irritating, they are generally to be preferred to the total absence of bonds. Here clothes make the man — not in a snobbish sense but in the sense that a person in clothes of his own choosing is no longer so identical with his neighbor as when in a shapeless hospital gown.

They come — the halt, the blind, the truly ill, the hypochondriacs — and sit in the rows of benches where thousands have sat before. And though the present patients may not actually be conscious of those other thousands, there is about the place an atmosphere that weighs upon them and kills the usual impulse for groups of waiting people to enter into light conversation. They are mostly silent, not despondently, yet with the very human fear of coming face to face with the so long ignored enemy within. Today — in a few moments even — the enemy may be given a dread name so that it can no longer be ignored.

There are several floors of the clinic — each with its wide central hall filled, like a church, with straight, high-backed benches. Upon the walls high above these are painted in huge ominous black letters lists of all the organs which may be affected by human ailments — ear, nose, throat, heart, eye, and related medical specialties — so on in a bewildering array of the possibilities of failure in the function of the human body.

In charge is an alert, competent person, Miss Florence Denver by name, who will take you inside the numbered doors that line the central waiting room. Here, for a start, is where medical diagnoses are made — long rows of examining tables with curtains to draw about each as privacy is needed. Visiting physicians come here — salaried men who see no more than three patients a day and who may order whatever tests are needed to aid in diagnosis without having to inquire into the patient's ability to pay.

You glance into the diagnostic laboratory and move along through various clinics, viewing fabulously expensive equipment, talking with nurses and patients. Here is the eye clinic where a patient is still undergoing examination. You slip quietly onto a stool and watch the procedure.

She's a woman of middle age, vigorously built, facing a young doctor who wears on his head a circular mirror like an off-center halo. He holds a light to one of her eyes, studying her carefully while he puts her at ease by a flow of conversation that, incidentally, draws out her story.

"Any trouble with that right eye?" he inquires casually.

"Oh, yes. I can't hardly see out of it at all — everything seems under a cloud —"

"Been that way long?"

She wrinkles her forehead. " 'Bout twenty years, I guess —"

Doctorlike, he makes no comment and you glance swiftly at him and at the nurse, whose expression shows no surprise. They must get accustomed to anything here, you guess — even to twenty years of unattended blindness.

"How did you happen to come in just today?" the doctor continues his examination as he asks this almost casually.

She considers her answer. "Well, the other eye ain't so good no more. So I thought mebbe I'd ought to do something . . ."

Twenty years! There are not many enemies that will wait so long with such sinister patience. Will that waiting give this one the margin of victory? Or will the medical knowledge and nursing care embodied in modern clinic and hospital still hold it at bay?

Was it ignorance that kept this woman waiting so long?

Ignorance that her handicap might increase — ignorance that anything could be done about it? Or was it fear? Or were there family complications that held her back? And how would any or all of these affect her acceptance of treatment and her final recovery? These are questions that may be ignored in the ward but must be acknowledged in a clinic patient, who, if improperly handled, may never return — may remain away to become a community burden as well as a community responsibility.

The only truly untroubled ones here are the babies and children waiting for pediatrics clinic under the eye of harassed elders. One has an arm in a sling, another seems to be covered with an angry red rash, another emerging from the examining room goes running up the hall, his billowing johnny revealing most of the unconcerned child beneath. Life for these may have temporary discomforts and passing problems. But, childlike, they live only in the present. The past for them is as gone as a storm of yesterday and the future is beyond their range of vision.

But their future is a problem — if not for them, then for their parents, or if not for their parents, then for the community as a whole. Will they grow into healthy, useful citizens or will they return here again and again, with chronic illnesses that proper care in proper time might have avoided? This is a question that becomes painfully urgent as the clinic patients come and go.

Between calls that are constantly coming to her desk, Miss Denver tries to explain it all to you. Here, she says, is where the student nurse first begins to envision her patient's personal problems and sees her work as a whole, sees the interaction of patient and community and hospital. The almost identical figures in those rows of identical hospital beds now become people whose situations are intimately affected by other people with whom they may have bonds or by the tragic absence of such bonds. Here, if she has sufficient power of perception, the young nurse may look down wide new vistas of endeavor and achievement.

"And that, I gather, is public health work?" you question. "I presume it's your business to interest them in that?"

"Well, I do try to develop any interests they may have. It may be, you know, that these girls will do public health work whether they plan to or not. Maybe they'll marry and settle down and think their nursing days are over. Perhaps they'll be in small towns where there are no adequate hospitals and where nurses are needed — in homes or in schools — and then they'll be back at work. We try to keep that in mind and prepare them for it. For instance, we make special efforts to have them taught how to draw blood from the veins of our diabetic patients —"

"But there wouldn't be very many diabetics needing blood tests in the kind of towns you describe! That couldn't be so very urgent."

"No, you're right. But when a girl has learned to do that, she's learned to put a needle into a vein without hurting and then when it comes to intravenous injections or blood transfusions — she knows how to go about it."

"You sound like a public health enthusiast," you comment. "I'd like to know how a nurse prepares herself for such work."

"I had the usual nurse's training," she explains, then adds proudly, "and I took special training for this kind of job at the Henry Street Settlement in New York. You've heard about it, of course . . ."

Of course. The Henry Street Settlement — what a tremendously significant name for the public welfare of our land.

How many vital health movements had their origins there!
How many of our leading nurses say, as did Miss Denver,
"I took special training at the Henry Street Settlement . . ."
Surely it must have its place in any story of nursing in Amer-
ica, if not in the whole world.

CHAPTER XVIII

Health and Henry Street

A sick woman in a squalid rear tenement, so wretched and so pitiful that, in all the years since, I have not seen anything more appealing, determined me, within half an hour to live on the East Side.

I had spent two years in a New York training-school for nurses, strenuous years for an undisciplined, untrained girl, but a wonderful human experience . . .[1]

Thus Lillian Wald begins the story of her life's work, which is also the story of the birth and growth of the Henry Street Settlement and of the visiting-nurse service in the city of New York. This was the kind of service which, as early as 1859, William Rathbone of Liverpool, England — philanthro-

[1] *The House on Henry Street.*

pist and friend of Dorothea Dix — had tried, with the advice
and assistance of Florence Nightingale, to establish in his own
city.

On our side of the Atlantic, the organization of a visiting-
nurse service was not undertaken until nearly twenty years
later. In 1877, the Woman's Branch of the New York City
Mission began to send trained nurses into the homes of the
sick poor. Unfortunately this service was doubly hampered,
first by the fact that it was a purely voluntary service and,
more important, by the fact that in that year there were, in
the whole country, too few trained nurses to make such a service truly effective. But the idea was growing, so that the
years 1885 and 1886 saw district-nurse organizations founded
in Buffalo, Boston, and Philadelphia.

These movements were all small and of only limited effectiveness but they showed that reform was in the air. The world,
so recently shaken by revolutions scientific and political, was
now in the process of a social revolution; conscientious and
high-minded citizens of means and culture could no longer
ignore the degrading slums at their doors. Lillian Wald —
trained, alert, idealistic — grown to maturity at this critical
time, was one of those whom both inheritance and environment had destined to do something about it.

The attractive daughter of a more than comfortable home —
was it only the shocking contrast between the ease and grace
of her own background and the sordid world of the underprivileged in the New York of 1893, so suddenly revealed to
her eyes, that determined her? So roused was she that she
tossed away without regret the future promised in the medical
studies she had embarked upon.

She mentions no other reason, yet she may unconsciously
have been influenced by that now almost legendary person,

Florence Nightingale, who had — in that same year, 1893 — written and published a paper to be presented to a Congress on Woman's Mission at the Chicago World's Fair. This paper, entitled "Sick-Nursing and Health-Nursing," contains the essential ideas embodied in all public health nursing of our day, over sixty years later:

> But since God did not mean mothers to be always accompanied by doctors, there is a want older still and larger still [than sick-nursing] . . . Call it *health-nursing* or general nursing — what you please. Upon womankind the national health, as far as the household goes, depends . . . And woman, the great mistress of family life, by whom everybody is born, has not been practically instructed at all. Everything has come before health.
>
> .   .   .   .
>
> In the future, which I may not see, for I am old, may a better way be opened! May the methods by which *every* infant, *every* human being, will have the best chance of health — the methods by which *every* sick person will have the best chance of recovery, be learned and practiced! Hospitals are only an intermediate stage in civilization, never intended, at all events, to take in the whole sick population.
>
> May we hope that the day will soon come when every mother will become a health-nurse and every poor sick person will have the opportunity of a share in a district sick-nurse at home! . . .

Conscious or not of this as an inspiration, it was to the realization of this hope that Lillian Wald was to dedicate most of her life — making her a pathfinder in new fields of nursing, taking her into welfare work, so that she became a revered leader for hundreds of nurses and social workers who tried to follow in her footsteps.

Lillian Wald's grandparents came from Germany in the

great period of the eighteen-fifties that brought to our shores so many distinguished and idealistic men and women who perceived tyranny steadily encroaching upon the liberties of their homeland and turned away from it to seek the freedom and enlarging opportunities of the New World.

Born in Ohio in the year 1867, Lillian grew up in a prosperous home full of warmth and affection. She had the happiest of childhoods. The closest view the little Lillian had of poverty was in the tramps who flocked for handouts to Mrs. Wald's notoriously generous back door. Every down-and-outer knew that here he would not be turned away empty-handed. How many of these drifters, one wonders, were flotsam tossed up in the aftermath of the storm of the Civil War? Did any of these tell the bright-eyed little girl of the fields they fought and the cause they served? In any case, great ideas were still in the air and must have been soberly discussed in a family like the Walds.

Lillian had reached the age of twenty-two without finding any special direction for her life, when she visited the home of a married sister who had recently had a baby. There she met her destiny in the person of a nurse who was a graduate of the Bellevue Hospital School of Nursing. History does not state who this nurse was nor precisely what she said. Perhaps she had some very special qualities of mind and person or perhaps her disciplined, poised self-assurance in a home otherwise dominated by excitement stirred the young woman to admiration. Besides, the nurse must have felt herself the apostle of a new and dedicated creed. Remember, it was only sixteen years since the first student had won through to a nurse's diploma. — Very likely the nurse spoke as such apostles have always done down through the ages.

This, in any case, was the turning point of Lillian Wald's

life. Here, she decided impulsively, was just the kind of life's work she had been seeking. Her parents were not so easily decided. The thought of their spoiled, talented daughter's undertaking such a strenuous career must have come as a shock to them. But they, too, were idealistic and could understand and sympathize with the impulse even while they marveled at their daughter's choice.

In the fall of 1889, with her parents' consent, Lillian entered the New York Hospital training school as a probationer. As she expressed it later, she had then "little more than an inspiration to be of use some way or somehow, and going to the hospital seemed the readiest means of realizing my desire." [2] Two years later — for at that time the course had not been lengthened to three years — she graduated.

To Lillian Wald, the hardest part of those two years was not the actual work. Her main problem was adjusting to the discipline necessary to the running of a big hospital. In addition she found the routine infinitely dull. But the wise superintendent, who may have perceived the seeds of greatness in the rebellious girl, patiently tamed her — teaching her the need for routine and rules in a hospital where many people had to work together for the good of many more.

This was the first and undoubtedly the hardest lesson for the undisciplined girl to master. She succeeded, however, and in the end became a fine nurse. Spoiled though Lillian once may have been, she was always a woman of character. What she started, she finished. So, in 1891, she duly graduated with her class and freed herself forever from the irritating restrictions of hospital life.

She did not, it seems, wish to free herself entirely from the care of the sick. Though the routine and discipline of

[2] *The House on Henry Street.*

hospital life repelled her and private-duty nursing in homes of wealth had no appeal, there must be something she could do. After considerable thought, she decided to study medicine and become a physician in her own right.

It was while she was enrolled as a student in the Women's Medical College in New York that a philanthropic friend approached her, asking her to go down into the slums to teach a Sabbath-school class in home nursing. This appealed to Lillian, so she readily agreed. Keeping in mind the kinds of people who came to visit the patients in the wards at the New York Hospital, she planned a course in home nursing that might give them what they needed. The classroom was in an old building on Henry Street.

This was to be first time, though not the last, that she was to meet those people in their native haunts. The slums must have had a shocking impact upon her sensitive mind. The crowding, the dirt, the disease — all these her trained eye could too easily perceive. And her trained mind could gradually estimate their effect upon morale as well as upon health. The climax came, as climaxes usually do, in one soul-shaking personal experience:

> From the schoolroom where I had been giving a lesson in bed-making, a little girl led me one drizzling March morning. She had told me of her sick mother, and gathering from her incoherent account that a child had been born, I caught up the paraphernalia of the bed-making lessons and carried it with me.
>
> The child led me over broken roadways . . . over dirty mattresses and heaps of refuse . . . between tall, reeking houses whose laden fire-escapes, useless for their appointed purpose, bulged with household goods of every description . . .
>
> The child led me on through a tenement hallway, across a

court where open and unscreened closets were promiscuously used by men and women, up into a rear tenement, by slimy steps where accumulated dirt was augmented that day by the mud of the streets, and finally into the sickroom . . .[3]

In the sickroom Lillian found her patient lying upon an unclean bed, soiled with a two-day-old hemorrhage, and without any possibility of quiet or privacy. This was a two-room tenement that, as was not uncommon, housed nine people — a family of seven that eked out its income by taking in two boarders.

As Lillian Wald wrote from a memory still vivid many years later:

> That morning's experience was a baptism of fire. Deserted were the laboratory and academic work of the college. I never returned to them. On my way from the sickroom to my comfortable student quarters, my mind was intent on my own responsibility . . . and I rejoiced that I had had a training in the care of the sick that in itself would give me an organic relationship to the neighborhood in which this awakening had come.[3]

After lying awake all night, reflecting upon the horrors she had viewed, Lillian formulated a plan for dealing with the situation. Since this plan involved making others share her vision, it might have presented serious difficulties had her own emotions not been so deeply involved. As it was, she could speak with moving eloquence of the conditions in the slums and of how she hoped to do something about them. Within a day, she had persuaded a classmate from nursing school — one Mary Brewster — to share in the venture.

They were to settle in the slums as nurses, taking an inte-

[3] *The House on Henry Street.*

gral part in the social life there, contributing to the mass of
foreign-born people whatever might be of value in their own
American background. It was the same sort of plan that
underlay later work done in Henry Street, as well as other
settlement projects which were growing up in the cities of our
land — projects apparently unknown to the then groping Lillian but undoubtedly spurred into being by the same great
social influences. The Henry Street Settlement, while not the
very first to sponsor either district nursing or settlement work,
seems to have been the first to combine the two ideas into a
working whole.

The young nurses wasted no time on tracing the history of
the movement they were to start. In fact it never occurred
to them that they were starting a movement. They were merely
trying to fill the need of which they had become so dramati-
cally conscious. For a beginning, they obtained quarters with
a group of young women living in the newly formed College
Settlement in Rivington Street. There they remained during
the months of July and August.

In September, finally, they managed to locate quarters of
their own — "no easy task," as Miss Wald confessed in her
reminiscences, "as we clung to the civilization of a bathroom
and, according to legend current at that time, there were only
two bathrooms in tenement houses below Fourteenth Street." [4]
This, be it understood, meant a total of two bathrooms in the
whole area! At last they found a suitable place, where decent
young ladies might live, on a top floor, hence relatively light
and airy and more private than one on a lower floor might have
been. Painted floors with scatter rugs, good family furniture,
simple washable curtains, a Baltimore heater to warm the place,

[4] *The House on Henry Street.*

pictures, books, and comfortable chairs — these constituted the equipment of the little apartment.

Modest though the quarters must seem to anyone now reading Miss Wald's description, they looked luxurious beyond the wildest dreams of many who lived close by. A small boy from a basement apartment was their first guest for a simple, well-cooked meal. Tommie cannily remained to eat his fill, then rushed downstairs, eyes bulging with excitement, to inform his mother, "Them ladies live like the Queen of England and eat off solid gold plates!" What Tommie's idea of solid gold plates was, one can only try to guess.

The young nurses started in to work almost at once, always trying to give the people of their area, in so far as conditions permitted, the same kind of nursing care they might have received in the best hospitals. A few visiting nurses were already being sent out by fraternal organizations, but they were highly specialized and departmentalized. In a single home where such an organization might have contacts one nurse could be sent out for orthopedics, another for maternal health, another for tuberculosis. Thus several might be calling where one could do the work. Meanwhile other equally needy families could find no nurse's services available.

This new service was to be more effective and more personal. The young nurses planned to do all kinds of nursing and to make their services available to anyone at any time, whether they belonged to any organization or could pay the nominal fee requested or not. For those who needed it, it could be charity. For the proud ones who rejected charity, it was to be what they wished. It was first and foremost to be a community service.

At first the nurses found the going not too easy but they gradually made for themselves a respected place in the community life. Their work soon demonstrated that many of their patients were far better off at home under good nursing care than in the best hospital then available. Apparently the psychological factor — the feeling of being adrift from family ties — affected not only the ill in the hospital but the family at home. This was particularly true when the ill person was a wage earner, without whom the family might have little to eat, or the mother, whose presence might be the only influence to keep the overcrowded, impoverished family from falling apart.

Florence Nightingale, with her usual extraordinary insight, had foreseen and understood all this. She wrote in 1893:

District nurses nurse the sick poor by visiting them in their own homes, not giving their whole time to one case, not residing in the house . . . They work under the doctor who, however, rarely comes more than once a day, if so often. The district nurse must be a clinical clerk, and keep notes for him, and dresser as well as nurse. She must, besides, nurse the room — often in towns the family's only room — that is, put it in good nursing order, as to ventilation, cleanliness, cheerfulness for recovery; teach the family, the neighbour, or the eldest child to keep it so; report sanitary defects to the proper authority. If the patient is the wage-earner, and the case is not essentially one for the hospital, she often thus prevents the whole family from being broken up, and saves them from the workhouse. If essentially a case for the hospital, she promotes its going there.

Though the district nurse gives nothing herself, she knows or ought to know, all the local agencies by whom indispensable wants may be supplied . . .

Having few or no hospital appliances at her disposal, she must be ingenious in improvising them.

She must, in fact, be even more accomplished and responsible than a nurse in a hospital . . .

. . . She also should be a health missioner as well as a sick-nurse.[5]

Health-nurses and health missioners, the visiting nurses of Henry Street always led a most strenuous life. "Enthusiasm, health, and uncommon good sense on the part of the nurse are essential," wrote Lillian Wald in the year 1915, "for without the vision of the importance of their task, they could not long endure the endless stair climbing, the weight of the bag, and the pulls on their emotions." [6]

[5] "Sick-Nursing and Health-Nursing."
[6] *The House on Henry Street.*

CHAPTER XIX

The Public Accepts the Public
Health Nurse

When the Henry Street Settlement work began in New York, and for a long time thereafter, impartial statistics were on the side of home treatments by visiting nurses. In 1913–1914, the now much enlarged Henry Street staff cared for 3535 cases of pneumonia, with a mortality rate of about 8 per cent as against over 31 per cent in the 1612 hospital-treated cases for the same period. To be just, however, one must remember that in the year 1914 almost 90 per cent of the sick remained at home, and that only the most desperate cases were likely to be sent to hospitals for care. Visiting nurses in the boroughs of Manhattan and the Bronx saw nearly 1100 more cases then than the total number treated in three large metropolitan hospitals taken together.

The venture that started out in 1893 with two volunteer workers had eleven workers by 1898, nine of them nurses. In 1900, there were fifteen workers and by 1906 the total had risen to twenty-seven. In 1931 there were about 16,000 public health nurses in the whole country, and in 1945 there were 275 working in the metropolitan area of New York alone. Visiting nurses had become an important and almost inseparable part of metropolitan life in our land.

As the concept of visiting nursing became accepted throughout New York, the scope of the work widened and it appealed to increasing numbers of women. And as increasing numbers of graduate nurses went into the work, they found its demands so different from what they had been accustomed to in hospitals that they became conscious of the need for special training. Enthusiasm, health, and uncommon good sense — all these were necessary; but special training would immensely increase their effectiveness.

Already in 1910, Teachers College of Columbia University in New York began to offer special advanced training to nurses interested in taking up public health work. Lecture courses on various aspects of public health were given at the college, which had made a co-operative agreement with the Henry Street Settlement whereby the students might also gain practical field experience. Since then women from all over the world have come to work and study there, giving added weight to the statement once made by the famous bacteriologist, Dr. William Welch, that one of America's most original contributions to public health was the public health nurse.

That sick woman in the squalid rear tenement changed not only the course of Lillian Wald's life but also the course of nursing history. A nurse trained to observant care of the sick could not possibly work in dirty, crowded tenements without realizing that, unsupported by other work, her best nursing efforts must prove all but in vain. She would also have to become something of a social worker and teacher — a "health missioner" — a campaigner for clean homes and for conditions that would make it possible to maintain such homes — for decent streets free of rubbish and decaying garbage, for policing that would remove from those streets some of the city's most vicious influences, for prompt diagnosis and isolation of menacing contagious diseases.

Lillian Wald, daughter of ease and luxury, was becoming just this kind of campaigner. And more, too — for her ever widening vision perceived new and unexplored areas. The plight of children, the next generation of Americans, began to concern her deeply. Here was a lad sent home from much needed schooling because of an infectious condition of the scalp that no one was doing anything to cure. A school nurse could have seen the infection in time, could have called the doctor's attention to it, could have supervised treatment so that the boy's education need not have been seriously interrupted. A school nurse, too, could have prevented the return to school of another lad recently ill with scarlet fever — in those days a most serious contagious disease — still shedding scales which might carry the illness to others.

Yes, a school nurse could protect both ill and well children — except for the fact that up to the year 1902 school nurses were unheard of. Miss Wald, having conceived the idea, saw to it that they were heard of. In 1902, as a demonstration, she assigned one of her Henry Street nurses to one public school. During the strenuous first month, that nurse gave 883 treatments, made 137 home visits, and treated successfully 25 children who had been sent home and kept home because of unattended ailments. This record convinced the Board of Health, and the school nurse as a national institution was born.

Once involved in the social aspects of nursing, it was only to be expected that the director of the settlement house on Henry Street should go still deeper into the matter and continue her campaigning for opportunities for children — first in her immediate environment in the New York slums, presently in the whole country. She threw herself into this, pleading for public parks and playgrounds to keep children off the dirty streets and away from the cramped quarters that made the usual energetic, healthy games of childhood impossible.

She campaigned, too, for the passing and enforcing of reasonable child labor laws so that the young might have a chance to develop without exploitation and its accompanying exhaustion, which so often meant ultimate destruction by contagious diseases, particularly tuberculosis. In the end, Lillian Wald brought about the establishment of the United States Children's Bureau.

It had come to her attention that the Secretary of Agriculture was about to make a trip to investigate the devastation caused in the Southern cotton crop by the invading Mexican boll weevil. Why, she wondered, should cotton bolls be a reasonable concern of government officials when the country's children were ignored? Once having conceived the idea, she went into action as usual, asked the question publicly and worked with unquenchable energy until in 1912, seven years later, she saw the Federal Children's Bureau created by act of Congress.

Extending her interests beyond city areas, Lillian Wald could visualize the needs of rural communities. In 1908, she suggested to the Red Cross the establishment of its Town and Country Nursing Service, which for many years carried skilled nursing and midwifery into isolated communities. She also managed to interest some of the larger insurance companies in providing visiting-nurse care for their industrial policyholders — proving effectively that good health meant good business for them.

Nowadays the idea of health-nursing is generally accepted even in communities that can as yet boast no nurse of their own. Where it is not an actuality, it is the dream of most remote areas to have residing with them a nurse ready to answer calls, in the town or on distant farms, as emergencies may require. For such a nurse, no place can be too remote or difficult of access. Exciting new adventure alternates with the familiar routine of sickroom or childbed. And wherever she goes, she enters as a friend.

In cities, the health-nurse meets other demands. Nowadays, because of the fine reputations of most hospitals, widespread hospital insurance, and the difficulties of home care where domestic help is almost impossible to obtain, so many people are flocking to hospitals that they are frequently overcrowded. The slightly sick holder of hospital insurance may now, against his will, have to remain at home under the occasional ministrations of a visiting nurse. The chronically ill, too, who otherwise might have to drag out their days in the drab monotony of institutional life, are an increasing source of calls for the nurse. The conditions of her work have changed with the years, but the need for her services goes on.

If trained and alert, the public health nurse may have great opportunities for checking the progress of disease before it has gone far. As both visitor and friend, she learns to know the family as a whole and to understand their needs in that intimate personal way few physicians can attain. Naturally, then, such a nurse should be an outstanding person.

In 1934, Miss Wald wrote:

> The nurses sent from Henry Street and similar organizations are very carefully selected for personality, and aptitude; their educational background is carefully investigated; they are given careful technical training before admission to the field, and are continually supervised by the more experienced members of the staff assigned to this duty.[1]

Small wonder that the words "Henry Street nurse" have such special meaning in the annals of nursing.

[1] *Windows on Henry Street.*

CHAPTER XX

From Henry Street to Hyden

Beginning with John Breckinridge, attorney general during Thomas Jefferson's administration, the name of Breckinridge has frequently been associated with some form of public service. John's granddaughter Margaret was mentioned with special honor in accounts of women who nursed during the Civil War. In our times, another descendant, Mary Breckinridge, has won renown for the nursing service she has brought to Kentucky mountaineers.

As a child and young woman — so she admits in her autobiography — Mary Breckinridge had no interest in becoming a nurse. Her life was too full and too happy for her to think of taking on a laborious profession. Born in Memphis, Tennessee, in the year 1881, she grew up in a loyally Southern family that had been deeply touched though not destroyed by the events of the Civil War. A decorative, much-traveled young lady, she had, at twenty-five, already been married and widowed. Vaguely ill at ease because she was almost too affectionately guarded by compassionate parents, she began to feel the need of some worth-while occupation.

Then it happened. She was visiting friends in North Carolina, when a child sickened with scarlet fever. She offered to stay by it. As she sat through the long hours of illness in that quiet room, she had plenty of time to think. She realized that there was absolutely nothing she was equipped to do for the little patient, and that the way to overcome such helplessness was to take nurses' training.

So, in the year 1907, Mary Breckinridge enrolled as a student in St. Luke's Hospital School of Nursing in New York. Student nurses of those days were expected to work long, hard hours without sufficient respite for meals and to be, at the same time, on occasional night call. As a result they often found themselves working in a daze of fatigue. Theoretically ten hours a day on duty was the limit, but they actually worked nearer eleven. Yet, while apparently tougher girls sickened under the strain, Mary Breckinridge was one of the four who graduated without having lost a day's work.

When World War I loomed, Mary Breckinridge naturally volunteered for nursing service with the American Red Cross. Since she had a brother in service, she was obliged to wait for special permission to go abroad — that was the regulation then. Meanwhile the terrible influenza epidemic of 1918 struck Washington, and Mrs. Breckinridge — one of the few trained nurses then available in the city — was put in charge of one of the five medical areas. Under her were five other nurses and hundreds of willing though hastily trained aides. Records had to be kept, help sent where most urgently needed — and always there were too few doctors and nurses to do half the things that needed doing.

When the epidemic was over, still no permission to go abroad had come through. Finally the war came to an end and the Red Cross canceled all sailings of personnel. But there were other ways to foreign service. The American Committee for Devastated France could use a person like Mrs. Breckinridge — fluent in French and trained in nursing, with special instruction in public health nursing that she had received at the Boston Instructive Visiting Nursing Association while waiting for her sailing papers.

For over two years she worked in devastated areas, helping distribute domestic and agricultural supplies to peasants returning to villages made almost uninhabitable by years of trench warfare. Always the plight of the children, most of them underfed, many orphaned, wrung her heart. She took positive steps to better it by organizing a child-hygiene and visiting-nurse service in her department.

By the time Mrs. Breckinridge sailed for home in 1921, she had acquired experience and wisdom, as well as the technique that was to make her successful in her chosen work. She had learned that a quite small new project, if properly tended, has a good chance of taking root and growing into something great and flourishing. By studying the customs and traditions of those among whom she worked, she could adapt her project to their needs. And where adaptation was unwise, she knew how to be gentle in combating long-cherished beliefs. She had, in other words, mastered the fundamentals of practical diplomacy.

She would need this special kind of diplomacy among the people in the region where she was to undertake her life's work.

Her interest was children — building up the health of children, first and foremost, then of their mothers and their whole families. It seemed to her that in remote and roadless areas children were especially, though unintentionally, neglected. So she decided she would work in the mountains of Kentucky and try to help people who were proud, ignorant of health facts, conservative in clinging to the ways and beliefs of their ancestors.

She would prepare herself carefully, studying the latest developments in public health nursing at Teachers College of Columbia University. Then she would spend a summer riding about the Kentucky mountains, learning firsthand of conditions there. After this she would study midwifery where it was a highly developed art — in England — and follow this study with visits to health stations in the remoter regions of the British Isles where a system was already established like the one she dreamed of for her Kentucky mountains.

Midwifery — the practice of assisting women during childbirth — is as old as childbirth itself. Only in comparatively recent years has it become a recognized part of medical practice and been dignified by the title "obstetrics." Fortunately, since in the more distant regions of this earth physicians are almost impossible to come by, most childbirths are normal and uncomplicated by anything beyond the power of a really skilled nurse to handle. The nurse, however, should have been trained to judge how much she herself can do and when a doctor must be called. As things were in the Kentucky mountains when Mary Breckinridge rode through them that summer, there was neither doctor nor nurse. Midwifery was practiced by some fifty-three women whose average age was about sixty — ignorant though well-intentioned, giving a care that was practically mediaeval.

This had been the state of affairs some forty years earlier in England when Florence Nightingale wrote a little book entitled *Introductory Notes on Lying-in Institutions Together with a Proposal for Organizing an Institution for Training Midwives and Midwifery Nurses.* She must also have talked about her ideas and must have been listened to eagerly by the young students at St. Thomas's Hospital, whom she always regarded as her special disciples. One of the early graduates of this school took special midwives' training, in so far as it was then available, and followed it with the founding, in 1881, of the Midwives' Institute.

The place where this nurse-midwife trained was in the British Lying-in Hospital. To the later descendant of this hospital — the British Hospital for Mothers and Babies in the Woolwich Dock area of London — Mary Breckinridge turned for the training she wanted. After four months, she received her midwife's certificate and went on her tour of the nursing stations of the Scottish Highlands and the Inner and Outer Hebrides — regions as wild, though in a different way, as the Kentucky mountains. Then another brief period of study in London — and she was at last ready to undertake her chosen work.

On May 28, 1925, a meeting was held in Frankfort, Kentucky, to organize the "Kentucky Committee for Mothers and Babies," presently to become the Frontier Nursing Service. From the start, provision was made for careful records and regular audits. Anyone who looks over the *Quarterly Bulletin* of the service and notes the meticulously kept accounts printed there cannot help being impressed by the thoughtful frugality with which donations are used.

Provision was also made, of course, for medical and hospital care and for the nurse-midwives who were soon to become the most essential part of the whole service. Dreaming of a future home in a well-equipped hospital and health center, the service started in Hyden, Kentucky, in a two-story building without modern plumbing but with an unpolluted well.

Interested friends soon began sending checks, and by spring, 1926, the organization was able to import its first nurse-midwife, an Englishwoman who almost turned and fled after her twenty-five-mile horseback ride from the railroad station. By August, two more nurse-midwives had arrived — one English and one a Texan trained in midwifery in England.

Nurses were engaged for other work too — for inoculating typhoid and diphtheria patients and for teaching them precautions so others need not be exposed to the diseases. If a nurse seemed to have aptitude for this rural work, arrangements were later made to send her abroad for training in midwifery, so that she might be more effective as a member of the Frontier Nursing Service team.

Plans for building a Hyden hospital and health center were progressing. This was no ordinary builder's problem, as anyone who has viewed the site can guess. Perched on mountainsides where they had to be anchored well above high water level and protected from recurring landslides, the buildings were constructed of stone and lumber, which were cheap and handled by masons and woodcutters who received low pay. But every modern convenience from cement to plumbing had to be hauled in over those long, steep roads at a dollar a hundred pounds. Skilled workmen to install such luxuries as plumbing had also to be brought in and at similarly high cost.

Utilities here, as in most mountain areas, also presented a serious problem. They had to get plenty of good, safe water yet dispose of a huge amount of sewage without the aid of a large metropolitan sewage disposal plant. Obtaining power for light and for running refrigerators, sterilizers, and X-ray machines was a constant problem for six years, until public power lines were at last run through the valley.

Meanwhile construction of the six outpost nursing centers went on. This work was supervised by nurses, inexperienced in problems of construction of any kind and constantly interrupted by calls for their professional services. Local committees gladly carried on, and local workmen took pride in their contribution to the health of their communities. Through their work some ten thousand people were, for the first time, to receive adequate nursing care.

By the end of 1930, five of these centers had been completed, each house planned so that one end might be used for a clinic and waiting room for visiting patients, and, when a patient appeared too ill to be moved, for a temporary hospital. The nurses residing in a center soon were accepted as belonging to each community, visited and called upon as occasion arose, offered neighborly tokens of appreciation such as pork when hogs were slaughtered and vegetables when the gardens were bearing well. It was the kind of neighborly relationship to be encountered in a rural community anywhere after the new resident has been accepted.

Once Hyden Hospital was completed, the worst cases — if they were able to travel — could be sent there. Transportation over rough, often slippery trails and unbridged rivers presented a constant problem. Yet women ready for childbed might ride in, sitting sidewise in the saddle, and seem none the worse for the experience. Nurses or couriers might bring in children across the pommels of their saddles. Or friends of the ill might arrange makeshift stretchers and bring them over the long, steep, difficult trails. Nowadays jeeps and trucks may be available for part of the trip if the weather is kind. Still, whatever the difficulties, they come — the sick, the expectant mothers, the wounded, the seriously burned, and those in need of emergency operations. For Hyden is their own hospital and they accept its services with joy in their hearts.

This is a truly rural hospital, belonging to its community in a very personal sense. Such a hospital has its own special problems, for, though small and intimate, it should be able to offer its community the same quality and variety of services available in a large metropolitan hospital. Yet, while it need not offer charity, it cannot hope to collect large fees.

Rural hospitals have very definite needs and responsibilities which must be faced and understood if rural communities are to receive the nursing care they need. The importance of this is now recognized by large metropolitan hospitals such as the Columbia-Presbyterian Medical Center in New York, which offers its nursing students an affiliation in rural nursing at a hospital in the upstate community of Cooperstown. And the girls' response is one of interest and enthusiasm.

Small though it is, Hyden Hospital has fine equipment as well as a good medical and nursing staff. In addition it has managed, by bringing in outstanding specialists from beyond the mountains, to offer the best of medical care in a wide variety of fields. It now also includes a graduate school of midwifery where nurses are trained to handle the demanding work of remote rural areas.

So carefully was the groundwork for this project laid and so conscientiously was it carried out that the Frontier Nursing Service has moved steadily forward from the rank of a purely local public health agency to a place famous throughout the world for its handling of the health problems of an isolated mountain region. From many lands people come — nurses and doctors and sociologists — to study the methods that have placed it among the foremost private public health agencies.

CHAPTER XXI

Nursing on the Near Frontier

The little town called Hyden is in Leslie County, Kentucky, where U.S. Route 421 and Kentucky Route 80 meet, coincide for some miles through a narrow mountain valley, to separate again as they emerge into the foothills. The road runs high above the valley bottom, clinging desperately to the shoulder of the steep mountain. The town has to be small, for there is no wide place to anchor any very large group of houses; and it is grimy with the soft coal which stains the slopes where it flows from many black gashes that are the mouths of small mines.

Drive along Route 421, with its steep grades and sharp turns, and you will see a bit of the still wild mountain country. Here is the vegetation of a not too fertile land, with corn hopefully planted on fields so nearly vertical that, as you look up at them, each row seems to grow out of the tops of the plants in the row below. You see scrubby second-growth forests stretching up into narrow side valleys where the sharp eye catches smoke rising from cabins probably no larger than the tiny log structures nestling here and there in sight of the highway. Along valley bottoms run streams, trickling in dry weather, swelling to wild torrents in the rains whose waters the steep, denuded slopes cannot hold back.

Over all this, from east of Harlan to the foot of the mountain where you meet Route 80, there is the odor of soft coal, so confusing to the city dweller who expects mountain air to be clear and clean. As you drive, uphill and down, taking the curves with the timorousness of an outsider, you meet, pass, or are passed by great trucks, full of coal or recently emptied, laboring up or speeding down the road. But whether you meet them or not, you are always conscious that they have passed that way, for your wheels drop into the deep troughs they have gouged in the tar surfaces and your transmission now and again drags ominously.

As you move along the main street of Hyden and come to the right-angled turn about the mountain shoulder, you will have an instant to glance out across the valley and see on the farther side a group of relatively large buildings, well constructed of stone or logs, one row of them seeming, like the rows of corn, to rest on top of another. If you stop to inquire of someone in the town, he will explain with visible pride that there is the Hyden Hospital and Clinic and the headquarters of its famous associate, the Frontier Nursing Service.

Day and night, in all weather, the visiting nurses of the Frontier Nursing Service are ready to answer calls for their help. Most of the nurses are also midwives. Naturally the nurse-midwife is better able to travel over the rough country than the mother-to-be, and often the mother, even if able to travel, cannot leave home with a quiet mind. In the *Quarterly Bulletin,* published by the Frontier Nursing Service, appear accounts of some of the more exciting moments in the never dull life of these nurses.

Bessie was expecting. This was a matter of moment not only to Bessie and to Bessie's husband Tom, but also to the nurse-midwife, who knew Bessie was counting on her to be on hand when the expected baby arrived. In fact, the coming event was possibly of even more moment to the nurse than to the parents-to-be, for the nurse lived on the far side of the river. It had poured all night and, typically, the river was already up over the road. Definitely it was a bad time for Bessie to be expecting, and the nurse pessimistically anticipated a call at about four in the morning.

> The morning wore on and I kept wondering about Bessie and if the tide in the river had beaten me in the race with Mr. Stork. A few hours later I received word from the local store at Stinnet that Bessie needed me. Expecting that Tom would wait for us at the Mouth of Stinnet, Lil and I tried to get started on our way.[1]

They got the service's jeep started but it soon stopped dead in the middle of the road; they had to abandon it right there, shoulder their bags, and hike to Stinnet. At Stinnet there was no Tom and no word of him, so they started off again down the river, "through cornfields and brush and over barbed wire fences."

At the edge of the swirling river, they stood and yelled for the ferryman, who did not like the idea of crossing the

[1] Anna May January, "Saturday's Child."

flood. However, he made it, to greet them with, "Me an' Jim just tipped [put a hole in the tip] the boat a little bit ago, can you'uns swim? Yon side is a fur piece when this ole river is actin' like this."

Hole and all, they embarked and crossed, "splashing, bucking and spinning against the waves." But they could not rest there.

> We shouldered the bags again and started trekking over rocks, through brush fences and up the mountain side, on through cornfields hanging precariously to the hillside. By this time I thought Tom had tried to cross the river and had been drowned and I kept gazing anxiously at the river, expecting to see a body or an upturned boat, but all I saw was logs and lumber sailing down. We trudged on and finally came to Bad Creek. There was nothing to do but wade, and wade we did with water up over our knees. We slushed up to Bessie's door and banged loudly. The door was calmly opened by Tom who said, "I was comin' to git you just as soon as I ate dinner. Bessie ain't punishin' much bad yit, but I thought we'd get you before the edge of dark."
>
> Bessie was calmly getting dinner, the cabin full of smoke. We took our seats on lard cans near the fire and proceeded to dry out a little — but not for long as Bessie began "punishin' bad." [2]

Some time later a bouncing ten-pound baby boy was born and Bessie could rest. Not so the nurses, who, in bitter freezing cold and dark, had to make their way back to the hospital before they could remove pants, socks, and boots stiff with ice.

This was all in the day's work to the nurse — possibly worse than some days, but no worse than many others. For she had

[2] "Saturday's Child."

gladly taken on work in a wild mountain region, and her reward was not only in the excitement and adventure of it but also in the knowledge that she was helping fill a great need.

Time was when some older local woman who had mothered enough children of her own to have had a variety of experiences, set herself up as midwife to assist younger neighbors. Kind though they may have been, such women knew as little of sterile techniques as their forebears of a century earlier. Having no training in scientific methods, they were guided more by superstition than by knowledge, so that many women suffered and died needlessly in childbirth. Young families were doomed to grow up without a mother's care. Sometimes, too, the babies were injured.

This can happen in many remote rural areas where hospitals are separated from patients by many miles of road as well as many more miles of roadless wilderness. Such isolation always breeds individualism, and one cannot expect individualists to accept hospitalization until education and example convince them that the strange-smelling places will actually contribute to their health and to the health of their children.

Even when generally accepted, hospitals can accomplish little of enduring value unless the people they care for are taught what causes illness and how it may be avoided. Polluted water supplies, unsanitary living conditions — these must be pointed out with infinite tact and patience, their dangers demonstrated, and means of correction suggested. The building of hospitals is only the beginning. People must be taught to use them, to call for nurses when they cannot reach the hospitals, and to listen to and follow the health suggestions doctors or nurses offer. Here, where the personal touch is so necessary, a privately financed organization can fill a real need.

CHAPTER XXII

The Remote Frontier

Far away though Hyden, Kentucky, may appear to the average city dweller of our land, it still is not far away in comparison with many parts of the world to which adventurous souls have carried medical and nursing care. In actual fact, almost anyone or anything may now be brought into or out of Hyden in a relatively short time. Hyden is never completely beyond the reach of our civilization and of its technical achievements.

Medicine and nursing have gone much farther afield, serving practically inaccessible areas of the Old and New Worlds; bringing along modern equipment when it has been physically or financially possible to do so, improvising resourcefully when it has not or when new kinds of emergencies have arisen. Whether in tropic, temperate, or arctic regions, these outposts all have in common great remoteness, often combined with difficult conditions of travel which make them all but inaccessible for long periods of the year. It may be the ice and snow of the north or the rain and heat of the tropics — the effect is much the same. Living conditions are often primitive and difficult, always strange.

In such places are new, unfamiliar people with the old familiar need for the ministrations of doctors and nurses. Stories told and written of these ministrations are always fascinating to us stay-at-homes. And though it would be hopeless to try to recount any large proportion of them, to recount none would leave the story of nursing quite incomplete. Let us, then, select just one place — unquestionably distant and difficult of access, where living conditions are rigorous compared with those of our civilization — and describe a bit of the work done there by the valiant people who have dedicated their lives to improving the health of its residents.

Such a place is Labrador and the northern shores of Newfoundland facing it across the Straits. Here would seem to be the bleakest and least hospitable spot upon which any outsider might choose to settle. Yet there the highly trained products of our modern civilization have gone, willingly and even eagerly undertaking work in an area where most of their civilization's refinements are, and will probably remain, unknown.

Not long after young Wilfred Grenfell made his first trip in the capacity of surgeon with the British fleet which was fishing in the waters off Labrador — over sixty years ago — he established his first hospital on shore. During the years since, the number of hospital stations has increased to five, with nursing stations set up in between and hospital boats carrying aid farther afield. The quality of medical, surgical, and nursing care has moved steadily forward, as doctors and nurses have willingly given their services for the smallest of material rewards.

The International Grenfell Association, whose responsibility it is to collect funds and run the business end of the undertaking, operates the only established medical and social service work for the trappers and fishermen and their families in some twelve hundred roadless square miles of Labrador and Northern Newfoundland. This area, whose coastal regions are served by a hospital ship, launches, and a supply boat, is divided into four medical districts with hospitals at key points and isolated nursing stations between. Nurses who volunteer for summer work in hospitals receive no pay at all beyond travel and living expenses. Minimal salaries are offered those who sign up for two years in hospitals or nursing stations. All this certainly doesn't sound very glamorous. Yet the Grenfell Association has never experienced a nurse shortage.

In her book already cited, Mary Williams Brinton devotes several chapters to a summer's experiences as a volunteer nurse in Labrador. A graduate of the school of nursing of the Presbyterian Hospital in Philadelphia, she had been serving as an industrial nurse for an electric company where the salary was good, the work easy, and the hours regular. Yet she tossed this all aside because of an irresistible impulse:

> As the excitement of the new job died down, the routine became humdrum and boredom developed from too much time on my hands. The idealism I had found in other branches of nursing was entirely lacking here, and when I tried to instill it, I found the people with whom I was dealing had a different approach . . . I felt if I stayed, the inner light might die

and ambition wane. When I heard that a nurse was needed at the Grenfell Mission in Labrador, I decided to make a change . . .[1]

An opportunity to keep that inner light alive was the priceless reward Dr. Grenfell and his struggling mission could offer the nurses who came to listen to his lectures as he toured the country in behalf of that mission. He tells in his autobiography of how he racked his brains for the most persuasive means of presenting the Labrador service to the young women in an audience at the Massachusetts General Hospital in Boston. Finally, he decided upon the description of a single incident in the life of one of his nurses.

One spring, he told them, his hospital received a telegram from a village about sixty snow-buried miles distant. The wire reported a very serious outbreak of influenza which needed a doctor's ministrations. But the doctor was also needed elsewhere, so a nurse volunteered and the villagers sent a dog team to bring her to them.

Two weeks later she telegraphed the hospital, begging for help in an even more serious emergency. One of her feverish patients — a skilled fish splitter — had gone out in a delirium, seized his fish-splitting knife, and split himself as effectively as ever he had his fish. Miraculously, he had not cut his intestines, but the situation was extremely critical.

The rivers were still too full of ice for navigation and the snow was too sticky for dog-team travel. The nurse would have to do the best she could without any medical assistance save advice telegraphed by the doctor sixty miles distant. So she went to work, after having persuaded the local priest to act as operative assistant.

[1] *My Cap and My Cape.*

That good man had such severe doubts of the outcome that he insisted upon first being permitted to administer the last rites. Then he took chloroform in hand and steadfastly administered the anesthetic while the nurse operated. She washed out the abdominal cavity with boiled water as best she could, returned the intestines more or less to their natural position, · and sewed up the wound sufficiently to prevent infection. The patient survived — first to make a trip to the hospital under the nurse's care, then to return to his family and his fishing, a well man.

When this account was finished, half the nurses in the audience were up, offering their services to the Grenfell Mission. Yet a nurse who accepted an appointment for two years of duty in Labrador had and still has to be prepared to face anything. Arriving in summer, she may help to open some of the stations closed during the long winters. Stoves have to be cleaned, floors and walls scrubbed, rust removed from clogged water pipes, stores unpacked — and in all this the nurse does her share. Naturally she makes up the hospital beds, sterilizes instruments, prepares such solutions as she thinks may be required — for no one is ever sure what emergencies may arise, only that they certainly will arise. Probably her first day is not past before she leaves the scrub pail to assist in the operating room.

Into this room come the most desperately sick and hurt; no one on that coast is likely to come near a hospital until things have passed far beyond the possibility of home treatment. This makes the work of doctors and nurses so much the harder both physically and emotionally. One does not easily become hardened to the pain inflicted while dressing old, deep, and infected wounds.

In winter, a nurse may be stationed either in one of the permanent hospitals, such as that at Northwest River, or in one of the isolated nursing stations. But no matter where she is, she must expect to take long trips to care for patients in their homes or to bring them to the hospital when necessary, and when travel may be possible.

Likely as not the trip out will end in a small, cold cabin where, again, the nurse may have to turn scrubwoman, wood-chopper, and housekeeper — in short, to quote Florence Nightingale, to "nurse the home." If the mother of the household is not sick, she usually is too preoccupied with caring for the sick in the family to do much in the way of housekeeping. The man of the family is probably away fishing or trapping. Alone, with only a team driver for company, the nurse makes rounds of the cabins that may need her help, advises expectant mothers, extracts teeth long since past the powers of any dentist to fill. And, as in the case of the nurse who took care of the fish splitter, she may even have to try her hand at emergency surgery.

Public health training is necessary for these appointments, as a great deal of responsibility must be undertaken by the nurse in charge. This applies to the nurses in charge of the nursing stations — and small wonder!

The summer work, too, has its quota of risk and excitement. These summer hospitals are situated in isolated spots where passing boats leave their sick, and people from distant outposts come steaming in, taking advantage of the summer's relative freedom of travel.

It was to the Battle Harbor Island summer station that, on a bright day of June, 1927, the then Mary Williams came for her volunteer service. Bleak though it was, the place had a wild, indescribable beauty — though beauty was something the newcomer found little time to enjoy.

"How would you like to run the operating room and give anesthetic?" I was asked the first day. The operation, a leg amputation for which proper instruments were lacking, made me realize how absolutely on our own we were. If the needed supplies were not on hand, there was no way of getting them — we had to improvise. . . .

During the years of my training, I never dreamed of meeting a situation like this. The operation took place in a cold corner room under the most extraordinary conditions. It was the doctor's first experience on his own, I was a novice in giving ether, and we were so shorthanded in desperation the dentist was called upon to help. . . . We were on our own and it brought out the best in us. Whatever skill and initiative we had counted . . . When the operation culminated successfully, we felt strangely elated.[2]

This, be it understood, was some years before the writer had taken her special training in anesthesiology!

A nurse's contribution to the health of the patients might become still more personal if the emergency demanded. Another incident of that summer in Battle Harbor describes such an occasion:

One of these sailing fleets going north left a very ill man with us. . . . Upon examination, the doctor decided a transfusion was his only chance. In our crude laboratory we had no accurate way of typing blood, but we came to the conclusion that Alberta Morbio, a nurse, had the best match. We understood the danger if our guess proved wrong, but realized we must go ahead. I shall never forget the scene. It took place in the men's ward, beautiful Alberta lying on the adjoining bed, her blood being transferred into his vein. . . . By this time, I realized what extraordinary results could be accomplished when circumstances were met by intuition and common sense, coupled with training and ingenuity . . . So

[2] *My Cap and My Cape.*

we managed to make him comfortable and pull him through a desperate illness.[3]

Some may ask what can be the lure of this kind of life — unremitting struggle against illness and suffering under the most impoverished and primitive of conditions. Is it not that here a nurse may really find herself? With none of the trimmings of civilization to distract from the main issues, here are heartwarming contacts with people and the chance to come close to them in their hours of greatest need. Where wild vistas open out endlessly, the human touch becomes even more precious, and those who love the wilds can serve their fellow man there in an intimacy that civilization inhibits.

[3] *My Cap and My Cape.*

CHAPTER XXIII

Health for All

In an age like ours, public health is no longer merely a local problem. In its strategy it must include the whole country if not the whole continent or, best of all, the whole world. We know that infection respects no boundaries, local or national, and that undernourishment and inadequate shelter may have their own violent political and international repercussions. In recent years, health agencies have either had to disband or to enlarge their outlook, for there has been a growing general awareness of health problems and a growing recognition that public health should be a reasonable preoccupation of law-givers. Appropriations for health activities can prove to be an economy rather than an extravagance.

In those towering Federal office buildings that rise in the midst of so many of our cities are housed the offices of various Federal agencies, among these the Public Health Service and the Children's Bureau. In each of these, public health nurses hold high office. They are women who have had wide training and experience and who now hold some of the highest positions open to women in any field. Let us visit the Regional Office of the Public Health Service in Center City.

On the twenty-second floor of the Federal Building is the suite that houses the United States Public Health Service. Miss Eleanor Davis, Senior Nurse Officer, has her office here. Her title is a reminder of the fact that workers in this service belong to the armed services and may be ordered about the country as necessity requires and without the possibly fatal delays involved in civilian shifts.

Her eyes sparkling with enthusiasm for her work, Miss Davis answers your questions in terms anyone could understand, for her work has taught her to be able to talk intelligibly to all kinds of people.

"Just what," you ask, "are the duties performed by the U.S. Public Health Service?"

"First and foremost," she answers promptly, "is the work in individual communities for the maintenance of health — sanitation and control of conditions that cause or encourage disease. Then there's the quarantine service in seaports particularly and the hospitals we maintain for merchant seamen —"

"Just for merchant seamen? Why should they especially rate it?"

"That's a good question. You know, they're the only group of people who may claim free hospitalization at any time."

"But why?"

"It goes way back. Ships used to dump their sick seamen at

the first port of call and sail away. Imagine what one abandoned and unrecognized case of smallpox or plague could — and did — do to the port and maybe the whole country!"

"Yes — I know epidemics used to start in seaports. I suppose the airplane has changed all that."

"Well, it's made the problem more general — of epidemics, I mean."

"And what about other hospitals — the Public Health Service has others, hasn't it?"

"Of course. You must have read about the places where narcotic addicts are treated — really psychiatric hospitals, you know. And then there's Carville in Louisiana where Hansen's disease — leprosy — is treated."

Carville! Everyone has heard about it — about its long history — about the new lease on life given people who everyone once believed were condemned to slow death.

How many centuries and worlds away from young Elizabeth of Hungary who took lepers into her castle and cared for them tenderly not only because she had disciplined her revulsion to the terrible effects of that disease but also because she was blissfully ignorant as to the means by which any disease was transferred from victim to victim! Had she herself lived ten years longer — long enough, perhaps, to perceive the first traces of the dread disease in herself, she still would not have understood the incredibly slow development of Hansen's bacillus in her own system. She would have searched her soul, recalling perhaps some secret loathing or unavowed sin, and considered herself duly punished by an all-knowing God. At the very least, she would have assumed that her human frailty was being put to some special trial of patience and faith.

In her era, the saintly Elizabeth could not possibly have expected to cure a disease that was considered some form of

divine punishment. Nothing could be done about cure until human enlightenment and human endeavor had placed the blame
where it belonged — on the extremely tiny bacillus which, in the
year 1871, a Norwegian physician named Hansen first identified. Then other human beings had to learn that the disease
is really no different from any other — that it is a curse
only as all disease is a curse, and much in need of medical research and nursing care. Drugs had to be found and methods of
administering them worked out, until today the centuries-old
disease is all but vanquished. Carville now is a monument to
the fact that by united effort in the cause of public health, and
by the establishment of public health services on a national or
even a world basis, almost any menacing disease may eventually be controlled.

As if reading your thoughts, Miss Davis goes on, "And then
we have special research projects in our Public Health Service.
A great research center has been set up at Bethesda, Maryland, for cancer and for cardiovascular diseases — heart and
circulatory troubles, you know. Then there's dental research
and research into problems of metabolism —"

"And where does nursing come in, in all this? I mean what
do the nurses in the service do?"

"Well, there's the nursing work in the various hospitals.
Then there are those like myself — nursing consultants. We're
supposed to keep up on the latest developments — in research,
or in health problems in general — and pass them on to
other nurses —"

"Other nurses? You mean others in the Public Health Service employ?"

"I mean to all nurses — and often to the general public, too.
Here, for instance, I work with State directors of nursing in an
area that includes six states. I try to help direct the planning of

an over-all health program — for nursing education, for hospital administration, and for the development of the various kinds of services that go to make up a good public health program. We have conferences, and give lectures — to nurses or the public, to schools and to mothers' groups, if they wish. And we give advice on health matters in general."

"Sounds like a big order."

"It is, I guess. But it's fun, too."

"Tell me, how does a nurse equip herself for this work? Advanced degrees and college training wouldn't be enough, would they?"

"Oh, we have to have certain background training and nursing experience. Then, after we get into the service we take part in a career-development program — being loaned to individual states to work in more limited areas until we have the necessary background and understanding."

"And what about your own training and experience — if you don't mind?"

"I started out to be a teacher but left that work when I became ill. After that nursing seemed to me like a good way to help people — so I trained."

"How did you get into public health nursing, then?"

She smiled a bit. "To tell you the truth, it began with me as a way to see New York. I worked at the Henry Street Settlement three and a half years, studying nights."

Ah, Henry Street again! "But it didn't take you three and a half years to see New York, did it?"

"Hardly. I knew pretty soon I wanted to be a public health nurse. I took night courses at Columbia University. Then the war came and I put in a stint of three years as a chief nurse in the navy. After that I went back and completed the requirements for a Master's degree, and since 1946 I've been in the Public Health Service."

"And what about the career-development program — did you get assignments under that?"

"Quite a few. I was educational director in a city of North Carolina, a State director of public health nurses in North Dakota, a regional consultant for the Public Health Service . . ."

Yes, she's been around. She knows her work from all angles and she knows how to work. Equally important, she's been given a chance to know the country in which that work must be done.

On the twenty-third floor of the same building is housed the Regional Office of the United States Children's Bureau, where, as Regional Nursing Consultant, Miss Harriet Roberts has her office. Alert, with a ready smile and a quick wit, she's the kind of person you'd be glad to have come into your home in times of stress. You know that without fuss or waste of words or energy, she'd give help just where and as needed, that her spirits could not easily be dampened, and that her shoulders would be competent to share the weight of your burdens without being bowed thereby. Even in an impersonal little office in a huge building filled with other offices, her personality shines out.

With ready informality, Miss Roberts agrees to explain her work. She is not, she tells you in answer to your first question, a Henry Street alumna. After graduating from the nursing school of the Woman's Hospital in Baltimore, she took special advanced training as a midwife in New York. And she's served as midwife, too, in all sorts of places.

"Midwife!" you exclaim. "That means you're one of those

people whose interest in children starts before their birth!"

"Where better to begin than helping the child to a healthy start?"

"Where indeed? But if that's the case where would the work of the Public Health Service end and that of the Children's Bureau start? I mean is there any part of public health work that doesn't affect — directly or indirectly — the health of children?"

"That's a good question," she agrees smiling. "Really, you know, any public health nurse spends from sixty to eighty per cent of her time in services to mothers and children — so our bureau really plays a pretty important part in public health problems in general. Only here the interest is not limited to health problems — though that's my special interest, of course — here we are concerned with all aspects of child welfare."

"You mean financial problems too?"

"Naturally — and it's hard to draw the line. I mean if there's a case of tuberculosis in the home, the family's health — and that means especially the children's — requires that the ill person be removed to a sanitarium. But if that ill person is the father and wage earner — or the mother, who is needed to hold the family together — then the problem becomes doubly acute."

Thus also spoke Florence Nightingale some sixty years ago!

"Of course," you agree. "Welfare worker and nurse would have to combine their efforts. But does the Federal bureau handle the millions of such details that must arise?"

"Not directly, but through the states and the agencies they maintain in individual counties or communities. Here we try to allocate Federal health funds for children to the states that have applied for them and whose plans for use we have checked and approved."

"Is that one of your jobs as a nurse?"

"Partly — on the consultation end, of course. Then, as a nursing consultant, I try to keep state agencies informed on new trends and ideas, meet with local nurses and advise them, lecture to groups of nurses or private citizens as they may want it. We conduct special institutes — on newborn infants, or maternal health, or special aspects of child care, such as mental health."

"And do you also train nurses for such special work — I mean do you use some of the funds for that?"

"Well, we try to encourage the states to undertake this — to establish scholarships for advanced training of public health nurses. The need is so great! In 1952 there were only about 26,000 public health nurses in the whole country — not more than 5,000 having been trained in the previous ten years."

"I gather you could use a lot more. But why the lack?"

"I don't really know. I guess it's because not enough students have been shown the fascinating opportunities in public health work."

"Tell me," you ask in the pause that follows, "who will do the bedside nursing in remote communities — or the visiting-nurse work in our cities — if the public health nurse is to be so occupied with plans and organizations? Or is that an indiscreet question?"

"It's a good question but we don't have a final answer yet. Bedside nursing can't be the responsibility of a Federal agency, so where State agencies don't like to get involved in such very personal work, private agencies have to carry on. As a matter of fact, there are not enough of these agencies. Fortunately, however, public agencies are beginning to face this more realistically and include bedside nursing along with their preventive work. That is, when they can find enough qualified nurses to handle both."

"But it sounds like such an interesting life. I'd think any girl would want to rush into it."

"It's never a dull life — that's sure. If a girl likes to do things and go places," she has a reminiscent look in her eye and a smile on her lips, "if she finds excitement and challenge in being called out any hour of day or night in fair weather or foul to start for some place she never before knew existed — if she enjoys new scenes and truly likes people, if she has a curiosity about life and is not timorous of soul — then I'd say to her, 'Train as a nurse, learn midwifery, practice it in the out-of-the-way communities where it is especially needed, and plan eventually to enter some central agency if you can.'"

"It sounds like rewarding work," you remark again.

"It is — and financially too, for that matter — in the end."

This time you wait quietly.

"But the real reward is something else," she goes on. "I guess I'd explain it this way. — Nowadays when I walk along a street and see a cripple struggling on crutches, perhaps trying to eke out a living selling pencils, I wish I could have been an active public health nurse when that person was young. Perhaps I could have perceived his trouble in time to have helped arrest it — perhaps all he needed was a little orthopedic care at the right time. Or if it was more serious, at least I could have taught him and his family how best to live with the handicap — could have helped him adjust to his environment so that now, instead of being a derelict selling pencils, he might be living a full, useful life. That," she murmurs reflectively, "would be the real reward."

They Can Do So Much

It is the month of May and tonight the senior class of the Center City Hospital School of Nursing is to receive its diplomas. These are the girls who more than two years ago won their caps and lit their candles of dedication. Look at them as they come marching down the aisle, faint smiles playing about their lips, eyes facing steadily forward. Behind them are the years of study and the wisdom accumulated in work — ahead of them the infinite possibilities of a profession with a glorious past and a great future. Now, the world is theirs for the grasping.

Tonight they will be told this — as all graduating classes everywhere are. And they will believe it not only because they want to but because they have learned they can meet life in its grimmest moments without flinching. They know that people will turn to them for help when the going gets hard. Upon their shoulders may often rest heavy burdens but in their hearts is the triumphant sense of achievement — the feeling that they can do so much.

Watch carefully as they go marching by. Can you not also sense that shadowy procession of unseen witnesses — the women who out of filth and ignorance and suffering created a high profession? Without their dedicated lives there could today be no such profession — no young women in white standing in proud array as their director rises to administer the nurse's oath.

Look yet again. Is there not beside the director a tiny, slim, auburn-haired figure in whose hand a lamp burns brightly? Is she not, perhaps, nodding gently as the young voices repeat the pledge that has so long been given her name:

"I solemnly pledge myself before God and in the presence of this assembly, to pass my life in purity and to practice my profession faithfully. I will abstain from whatever is deleterious and mischievous and will not take or knowingly administer any harmful drug. I will do all in my power to elevate the standard of my profession and will hold in confidence all personal matters committed to my keeping and all family affairs coming to my knowledge in the practice of my calling. With loyalty will I endeavor to aid the physician in his work, and devote myself to the welfare of those committed to my care."

Bibliography

Note: The following is a list of the more important works consulted in the process of preparing this book on American nursing. Admittedly, it is not a complete bibliography on the subject. There are, for instance, many histories of nursing, most of them written with the requirements of some special course in a special school or group of schools in mind. I have listed one of the earliest and most exhaustive, that of Nutting and Dock, and three other shorter ones that the reader might find easier to consult. I have read extensively in various journals not listed here, though anyone wishing to pursue studies in any special direction might find it advisable to consult such journals — usually available in the libraries of medical schools or in schools of nursing. These include the *American Journal of Nursing,* issued by the American Nurses' Association, *Nursing Outlook,* issued jointly by the National League for Nursing and Public Health Nursing, *Nursing Research,* issued by the National League for Nursing, and *Public Health Reports,* issued by the Public Health Service of the United States Department of Health, Education, and Welfare. For those interested in Canadian nursing, there is the *Canadian Nurse,* issued by the Canadian Nurses' Association.

The titles marked with an asterisk (*) are those from which direct quotations have been made or from which, lacking complete library facilities, I have taken material quoted from unavailable books or journals.

*ALCOTT, LOUISA M. *Hospital Sketches.* Boston: Little, Brown & Co., 1902. 102 pp. (First edition, Boston: J. Redpath, 1863.)

BAKER, NINA BROWN. *Cyclone in Calico: The Story of Mary Ann Bickerdyke.* Boston: Little, Brown & Co., 1952. 278 pp.

BARTON, CLARA H. *The Story of My Childhood.* New York: The Baker & Taylor Co., 1907. 125 pp.

*BARTON, CLARA H. *The Red Cross; a History of this Remarkable International Movement in the Interest of Humanity.* Washington, D.C.: American National Red Cross, 1898. 684 pp.

BARTON, WILLIAM E. *The Life of Clara Barton, Founder of the American Red Cross,* Vols. I and II. Boston: Houghton Mifflin Co., 1922. Vol. I, 398 pp.; Vol. II, 387 pp.

BOARDMAN, MABEL T. *Under the Red Cross Flag at Home and Abroad.* Philadelphia: J. B. Lippincott Co., 1917. 333 pp.

BRECKINRIDGE, MARY. *Wide Neighborhoods: A Story of the Frontier Nursing Service.* New York: Harper & Brothers, 1952. 366 pp.

BRIDGMAN, MARGARET. *Collegiate Education for Nursing.* New York: Russell Sage Foundation, 1953. 205 pp.

*BRINTON, MARY WILLIAMS. *My Cap and My Cape: An Autobiography.* Philadelphia: Dorrance & Co., 1950. 262 pp.

BROCKETT, L. P. *Woman's Work in the Civil War.* Philadelphia: Ziegler, McCurdy & Co., 1867. 799 pp.

*BROWN, ESTHER LUCILLE. *Nursing for the Future. A Report Prepared for the National Nursing Council.* New York: Russell Sage Foundation, 1948. 198 pp.

*CASTLEMAN, ALFRED L. *The Army of the Potomac. Behind the Scenes. A Diary of Unwritten History; from the Organization of the Army, by General George B. McClellan, to the Close of the Campaign in Virginia, about the First Day of January, 1863.* Milwaukee: Strickland & Co., 1863. 288 pp.

COOK, EDWARD TYAS. *The Life of Florence Nightingale,* Vols. I and II. London: The Macmillan Co., 1914 (privately printed). Vol. I, 507 pp.; Vol. II, 510 pp.

*CUMMING, KATE. *A Journal of Hospital Life in the Confederate Army of Tennessee from the Battle of Shiloh to the End of the War.* Louisville: J. P. Morgan & Co., 1866. 199 pp.

*CUMMING, KATE. *Gleanings from the Southland. Sketches of Life* *and Manners of the People of the South before, during, and after the War of Secession, with Extracts from the Author's Journal and an Epitome of the New South.* Birmingham: Roberts & Son, 1892. 277 pp.

DOCK, LAVINIA L. AND STEWART, ISABEL M. *A Short History of Nursing, from the Earliest Times to the Present Day.* Fourth revised edition. New York: G. P. Putnam's Sons, 1938. 436 pp.

DUFFUS, ROBERT L. *Lillian Wald, Neighbor and Crusader.* New York: The Macmillan Co., 1938. 371 pp.

DULLES, FOSTER RHEA. *The American Red Cross: A History.* New York: Harper & Brothers, 1950. 554 pp.

*DUNANT, HENRI. *A Memory of Solferino (Un souvenir de Solferino),* translated from the French of the first edition (1862). Washington, D.C.: American Red Cross, 1939. 95 pp.

*ELLIS, [Dr.] THOMAS T. *Leaves from the Diary of an Army Surgeon; or Incidents of Field, Camp, and Hospital Life.* New York: J. Bradburn, 1863. 312 pp.

*EPLER, PERCY H. *The Life of Clara Barton.* New York: The Macmillan Co., 1915. 438 pp.

*FLIKKE, JULIA O. *Nurses in Action, the Story of the Army Nurse Corps.* Philadelphia and New York: J. B. Lippincott Co., 1943. 239 pp.

GARDNER, CAROLINE. *Clever Country. Kentucky Mountain Trails.* New York: Fleming Revell Co., 1931. 159 pp.

GARRISON, FIELDING H. *An Introduction to the History of Medicine.* Philadelphia: W. B. Saunders Co., 1921. 942 pp.

GLADWIN, MARY E. *The Red Cross and Jane Arminda Delano.* Philadelphia: W. B. Saunders Co., 1931. 91 pp.

*GROSS, SAMUEL DAVID. *Remarks on the Training of Nurses.* Philadelphia: Collins, Printer, 1869. 15 pp.

*HOLLAND, MARY A. G. *Our Army Nurses.* Boston: B. Wilkins & Co., 1895. 600 pp.
flin Co., 1946. 305 pp.

HUGHES, LORA WOOD. *No Time for Tears.* Boston: Houghton Mif-

*JAMIESON, ELIZABETH M. AND SEWALL, MARY. *Trends in Nursing History.* Third edition. Philadelphia: W. B. Saunders Co., 1949. 632 pp.

JANUARY, ANNA MAY. "Saturday's Child," *Quarterly Bulletin, Frontier Nursing Service, Inc.,* Hyden, Ky., Spring, 1952.

KERNODLE, PORTIA B. *The Red Cross Nurse in Action: 1882–1948.* New York: Harper & Brothers, 1949. 524 pp.

KOCH, HARRIET ROSE. *Militant Angel* [Annie W. Goodrich]. New York: The Macmillan Co., 1951. 167 pp.

*LIVERMORE, MARY A. *My Story of the War: A Woman's Narrative of Four Years' Personal Experience as Nurse in the Union Army, and in Relief Work . . .* Hartford, Conn.: A. D. Worthington and Co., 1888. 699 pp.

Memoir of Susan Dimock, Resident Physician of the New England Hospital for Women and Children. Boston: privately printed, 1875. 103 pp.

MERRICK, ELLIOTT. *Northern Nurse.* New York: Charles Scribner's Sons, 1942. 311 pp.

*MUNROE, JAMES PHINNEY. *Adventures of an Army Nurse in Two Wars Edited from the Diary and Correspondence of Mary Phinney, Baroness von Olnhausen.* Boston: Little, Brown & Co., 1903. 355 pp.

*NIGHTINGALE, FLORENCE. *Introductory Notes on Lying-in Institutions Together with a Proposal for Organizing an Institution for Training Midwives and Midwifery Nurses.* London: Longmans, Green & Co., 1871. 110 pp.

*NIGHTINGALE, FLORENCE. *Notes on Nursing. What It Is and What It Is Not.* London: Harrison, 1859. 70 pp. (Reissued in New York by D. Appleton, 1860. 140 pp.)

*NIGHTINGALE, FLORENCE. "Sick-Nursing and Health-Nursing," in Burdett-Coutts's *Woman's Mission,* pp. 184–205. London: Sampson Low, Marston & Co., Ltd., 1893.

NUTTING, M. A. AND DOCK, L. L. *A History of Nursing,* Vols. I–IV. New York: G. P. Putnam's Sons, 1907–1912.

POOLE, ERNEST. *Nurses on Horseback.* New York: The Macmillan Co., 1932. 168 pp.

RATHBONE, WILLIAM. *Sketch of the History and Progress of Dis-*

trict Nursing, with an Introduction by Florence Nightingale. London: Macmillan, 1890. 132 pp.

* RICHARDS, LINDA A. *Reminiscences of Linda Richards, America's First Trained Nurse.* Boston: Whitcomb & Barrows, 1911. 121 pp.

ROBINSON, VICTOR. *White Caps. The Story of Nursing.* Philadelphia: J. B. Lippincott Co., 1946. 425 pp.

*SEYMER, LUCY RIDGELY. *A General History of Nursing.* Second edition. New York: The Macmillan Co., 1949. 332 pp.

* [Taylor, Fanny M.] *Eastern Hospitals and English Nurses; the Narrative of Twelve Months' Experience in the Hospitals of Koulali and Scutari, by a Lady Volunteer,* Vols. I and II. London: Hurst & Blackett, 1856.

THOMAS, ADAH B. *Pathfinders, a History of the Progress of Colored Graduate Nurses.* New York: [Kay Printing House] 1929. 240 pp.

*TIFFANY, FRANCIS. *Life of Dorothea Lynde Dix.* Boston: Houghton Mifflin Co., 1890. 392 pp.

WALD, LILLIAN D. *The House on Henry Street.* New York: Henry Holt & Co., 1915. 317 pp.

*WALD, LILLIAN D. *Windows on Henry Street.* Boston: Little, Brown & Co., 1934. 348 pp.

WEST, MARGARET AND HAWKINS, CHRISTY. *Nursing Schools at the Mid Century.* New York: National Committee for the Improvement of Nursing Services. 1950. 88 pp.

WILLIAMS, BLANCHE COLTON. *Clara Barton, Daughter of Destiny.* Philadelphia: J. B. Lippincott Co., 1941. 468 pp.

* WILLIAMSON, ANNA A. *50 Years in Starch.* Culver City, Calif.: Murray & Gee, Inc., 1948. 245 pp.

WOODHAM-SMITH, CECIL. *Florence Nightingale.* London: Constable, 1950. 615 pp.

YOST, EDNA. *American Women of Nursing.* Philadelphia and New York: J. B. Lippincott Co., 1947. 197 pp.

Index